GOD'S DESIGN® FOR CHEMIS...

TEACHER SUPPLEMENT

1:1
answers**ingenesis**
Petersburg, Kentucky, USA

ANSWERS IN GENESIS SCIENCE BY DEBBIE & RICHARD LAWRENCE

God's Design for Chemistry & Ecology Teacher Supplement

© 2008 by Debbie & Richard Lawrence

Published by Answers in Genesis, 2800 Bullittsburg Church Rd., Petersburg KY 41080

You may contact the authors at (970) 686-5744

ISBN: 1-60092-238-4

Cover design & layout: Diane King
Editors: Lori Jaworski, Gary Vaterlaus

The publisher and authors have made every reasonable effort to ensure that the activities recommended in this book are safe when performed as instructed but assume no responsibility for any damage caused or sustained while conducting the experiments and activities. It is the parents', guardians', and/or teachers' responsibility to supervise all recommended activities.

Printed in China.

www.answersingenesis.org   www.godsdesignscience.com

TABLE OF CONTENTS

TEACHER INTRODUCTION

WELCOME TO
GOD'S DESIGN® FOR CHEMISTRY & ECOLOGY

God's Design for Chemistry & Ecology is a series that has been designed for use in teaching chemistry and ecology to elementary and middle school students. It is divided into three books: *Properties of Matter*, *Properties of Atoms and Molecules*, and *Properties of Ecosystems*. Each book has 35 lessons including a final project that ties all of the lessons together.

In addition to the lessons, special features in each book include biographical information on interesting people as well as fun facts to make the subject more fun.

Although this is a complete curriculum, the information included here is just a beginning, so please feel free to add to each lesson as you see fit. A resource guide is included in the appendices to help you find additional information and resources. A list of supplies needed is included at the beginning of each lesson, while a master list of all supplies needed for the entire series can be found in the appendices.

Answer keys for all review questions, worksheets, quizzes, and the final exam are included here. Reproducible student worksheets and tests may be found on the supplementary CD-Rom for easy printing. Please contact Answers in Genesis if you wish to purchase a printed version of all the student materials, or go to www.AnswersBookstore.com.

If you wish to get through the Chemistry & Ecology series in one year, you should plan on covering approximately three lessons per week. The time required for each lesson varies depending on how much additional information you want to include, but you can plan on about 45 minutes per lesson.

If you wish to cover the material in more depth, you may add additional information and take a longer period of time to cover all the material or you could choose to do only one or two of the books in the series as a unit study.

WHY TEACH CHEMISTRY & ECOLOGY?

Maybe you hate science or you just hate teaching it. Maybe you love science but don't quite know how to teach it to your children. Maybe science just doesn't seem as important as some of those other subjects you need to teach. Maybe you need a little motivation. If any of these descriptions fits you, then please consider the following.

It is not uncommon to question the need to teach your kids hands-on science in elementary school. We could argue that the knowledge gained in science will be needed later in life in order for your children to be more productive and well-rounded adults. We could argue that teaching your children science also teaches them logical and inductive thinking and reasoning skills, which are tools they will need to be more successful. We could argue that science is a necessity in this technological world in which we live. While all of these arguments are true, not one of them is the real reason that we should teach our children science. The most important reason to teach science in elementary school is to give your children an understanding that God is our Creator, and the Bible can be trusted. Teaching science from a creation perspective is one of the best ways to reinforce your children's faith in God and to help them counter the evolutionary propaganda they face every day.

God is the Master Creator of everything. His handiwork is all around us. Our Great Creator put in place all of the laws of physics, biology, and chemistry. These laws were put here for us to see His wisdom and power. In science, we see the hand of God at work more than in any other subject. Romans 1:20 says, "For since the creation of the world His invisible attributes are clearly seen, being understood by the things that are made, even His eternal power and Godhead, so that they [men] are without excuse." We need to help our children see God as Creator of the world around them so they will be able to recognize God and follow Him.

The study of chemistry helps us understand and appreciate the amazing way everything God created works together. The study of atoms and molecules and how different substances react with each other reveals an amazing design, even at the smallest level of life. Understanding the carbon, nitrogen, and water cycles helps our children see that God has a plan to keep everything working together. Learning about ecosystems reveals God's genius in nature.

It's fun to teach chemistry and ecology! It's interesting too. The elements of chemistry are all around us. Children naturally like to combine things to see what will happen. You just need to direct their curiosity.

Finally, teaching chemistry is easy. You won't have to try to find strange materials for experiments or do dangerous things to learn about chemistry. Chemistry is as close as your kitchen or your own body, and ecosystems are just outside your door.

How Do I Teach Science?

In order to teach any subject, you need to understand that people learn in different ways. Most people, and children in particular, have a dominant or preferred learning style in which they absorb and retain information more easily.

If a student's dominant style is:

Auditory
He needs not only to hear the information but he needs to hear himself say it. This child needs oral presentation as well as oral drill and repetition.
Visual
She needs things she can see. This child responds well to flashcards, pictures, charts, models, etc.
Kinesthetic
He needs active participation. This child remembers best through games, hands-on activities, experiments, and field trips.

Also, some people are more relational while others are more analytical. The relational student needs to know why this subject is important and how it will affect him personally. The analytical student, however, wants just the facts.

If you are trying to teach more than one student, you will probably have to deal with more than one learning style. Therefore, you need to present your lessons in several different ways so that each student can grasp and retain the information.

Grades 3–8

Each lesson should be completed by all upper elementary and junior high students. This is the main part of the lesson containing a reading section, a hands-on activity that reinforces the ideas in the reading section (blue box), and a review section that provides review questions and application questions (red box).

Grades 6–8

For middle school/junior high age students, we provide a "Challenge" section that contains more challenging material as well as additional activities and projects for older students (green box).

We suggest a threefold approach to each lesson:

Introduce the topic

We give a brief description of the facts. Frequently you will want to add more information than the essentials given in this book. In addition to reading this section aloud, you may wish to do one or more of the following:

- Read a related book with your students.
- Write things down to help your visual students.
- Give some history of the subject. We provide some historical sketches to help you, but you may want to add more.
- Ask questions to get your students thinking about the subject.

Make observations and do experiments

- Hands-on projects are suggested for each lesson. This section of each lesson may require help from the teacher.
- Have your students perform the activity by themselves whenever possible.

Review

- The "What did we learn?" section has review questions.
- The "Taking it further" section encourages students to
  - Draw conclusions
  - Make applications of what was learned
  - Add extended information to what was covered in the lesson
- The "FUN FACT" section adds fun or interesting information.

By teaching all three parts of the lesson, you will be presenting the material in a way that all learning styles can both relate to and remember.

Also, this approach relates directly to the scientific method and will help your students think more scientifically. The *scientific method* is just a way to examine a subject logically and learn from it. Briefly, the steps of the scientific method are:

1. Learn about a topic.
2. Ask a question.
3. Make a hypothesis (a good guess).
4. Design an experiment to test your hypothesis.
5. Observe the experiment and collect data.
6. Draw conclusions. (Does the data support your hypothesis?)

Note: It's okay to have a "wrong hypothesis." That's how we learn. Be sure to help your students understand why they sometimes get a different result than expected.

Our lessons will help your students begin to approach problems in a logical, scientific way.

HOW DO I TEACH CREATION VS. EVOLUTION?

We are constantly bombarded by evolutionary ideas about the earth in books, movies, museums, and even commercials. These raise many questions: Is a living being just a collection of chemicals? Did life begin as a random combination of chemicals? Can life be recreated in a laboratory? What does the chemical evidence tell us about the earth? The Bible answers these questions, and this book accepts the historical accuracy of the Bible as written. We believe this is the only way we can teach our children to trust that everything God says is true.

There are five common views of the origins of life and the age of the earth:

Historical biblical account	Progressive creation	Gap theory	Theistic evolution	Naturalistic evolution
Each day of creation in Genesis is a normal day of about 24 hours in length, in which God created everything that exists. The earth is only thousands of years old, as determined by the genealogies in the Bible.	The idea that God created various creatures to replace other creatures that died out over millions of years. Each of the days in Genesis represents a long period of time (day-age view) and the earth is billions of years old.	The idea that there was a long, long time between what happened in Genesis 1:1 and what happened in Genesis 1:2. During this time, the "fossil record" was supposed to have formed, and millions of years of earth history supposedly passed.	The idea that God used the process of evolution over millions of years (involving struggle and death) to bring about what we see today.	The view that there is no God and evolution of all life forms happened by purely naturalistic processes over billions of years. Ken Ham et al., *The Answers Book*, (El Cajon: Master Books, 2000), 33–76.

Any theory that tries to combine the evolutionary time frame with creation presupposes that death entered the world before Adam sinned, which contradicts what God has said in His Word. The view that the earth (and its "fossil record") is hundreds of millions of years old damages the gospel message. God's completed creation was "very good" at the end of the sixth day (Genesis 1:31). Death entered this perfect paradise *after* Adam disobeyed God's command. It was the punishment for Adam's sin (Genesis 2:16–17; 3:19; Romans 5:12–19). Thorns appeared when God cursed the ground because of Adam's sin (Genesis 3:18).

The first animal death occurred when God killed at least one animal, shedding its blood, to make clothes for Adam and Eve (Genesis 3:21). If the earth's "fossil record" (filled with death, disease, and thorns) formed over millions of years before Adam appeared (and before he sinned),

then death no longer would be the penalty for sin. Death, the "last enemy" (1 Corinthians 15:26), diseases (such as cancer), and thorns would instead be part of the original creation that God labeled "very good." No, it is clear that the "fossil record" formed sometime *after* Adam sinned—not many millions of years before. Most fossils were formed as a result of the worldwide Genesis Flood.

When viewed from a biblical perspective, the scientific evidence clearly supports a recent creation by God, and not naturalistic evolution and millions of years. The volume of evidence supporting the biblical creation account is substantial and cannot be adequately covered in this book. If you would like more information on this topic, please see the resource guide in the appendices. To help get you started, just a few examples of evidence supporting biblical creation are given below:

Evolutionary Myth: Life evolved from non-life when chemicals randomly combined together to produce amino acids and then proteins that produced living cells.

The Truth: The chemical requirements for DNA and proteins to line up just right to create life could not have happened through purely natural processes. The process of converting DNA information into proteins requires at least 75 different protein molecules. But each and every one of these 75 proteins must be synthesized in the first place by the process in which they themselves are involved. How could the process begin without the presence of all the necessary proteins? Could all 75 proteins have arisen by chance in just the right place at just the right time? Dr. Gary Parker says this is like the chicken and the egg problem. The obvious conclusion is that both the DNA and proteins must have been functional from the beginning, otherwise life could not exist. The best explanation for the existence of these proteins and DNA is that God created them.

See Gary Parker, *Creation: Facts of Life* (Green Forest, Arkansas: Master Books, 2006), 20–43.

Evolutionary Myth: Stanley Miller created life in a test tube, thus demonstrating that the early earth had the conditions necessary for life to begin.

The Truth: Although Miller was able to create amino acids from raw chemicals in his famous experiment, he did not create anything close to life or even the ingredients of life. There are four main problems with Miller's experiment. First, he left out oxygen because he knew that oxygen corrodes and destroys amino acids very quickly. However, rocks found in every layer of the earth indicate that oxygen has always been a part of the earth's atmosphere. Second, Miller included ammonia gas and methane gas. Ammonia gas would not have been present in any large quantities because it would have been dissolved in the oceans. And there is no indication in any of the rock layers that methane has ever been a part of the earth's atmosphere. Third, Miller used a spark of electricity to cause the amino acids to form, simulating lightning. However, this spark more quickly destroyed the amino acids than built them up, so to keep the amino acids from being destroyed, Miller used specially designed equipment to siphon off the amino acids before they could be destroyed. This is not what would have happened in nature. And finally, although Miller did produce amino acids, they were not the kinds of amino acids that are needed for life as we know it. Most of the acids were ones that actually break down proteins, not build them up.

See Ken Ham, et al., *War of the Worldviews* (Green Forest, Arkansas: Master Books, 2006), 15–24. See also www.answersingenesis.org/go/origin.

Evolutionary Myth: Living creatures are just a collection of chemicals.

The Truth: It is true that cells are made of specific chemicals. However, a dead animal is made of the same chemicals as it was when it was living, but it cannot become alive again. What makes the chemicals into a living creature is the result of the organization of the substances, not just the substances themselves. Dr. Parker again uses an example. An airplane is made up of millions of non-flying parts; however, it can fly because of the design and organization of those parts. Similarly, plants and animals are alive because God created the chemicals in a specific way for them to be able to live. A collection of all the right parts is not life.

Evolutionary Myth: Chemical evidence points to an earth that is billions of years old.

The Truth: Much of the chemical evidence actually points to a young earth. For example, radioactive decay in the earth's crust produces helium atoms that rise to the surface and enter the atmosphere. Assuming that the rate of helium production has always been constant (an evolutionary assumption), the maximum age for the atmosphere could only be 2 million years.[1] This is much younger than the 4+ billion years claimed by evolutionists. And there are many ideas that could explain the presence of helium that would indicate a much younger age than 2 million years. Similarly, salt accumulates in the ocean over time. Evolutionists claim that life evolved in a salty ocean 3–4 billion years ago. If this were true and the salt has continued to accumulate over billions of years, the ocean would be too salty for anything to live in by now. Using the most conservative possible values (those that would give the oldest possible age for the oceans), scientists have calculated that the ocean must be less than 62 million years. That number is based on the assumption that nothing has affected the rate at which the salt is accumulating. However, the Genesis Flood would have drastically altered the amount of salt in the ocean, dissolving much sodium from land rocks.[2] Thus, the chemical evidence does not support an earth that is billions of years old.

[1] Dr. Don DeYoung, *Thousands…not billions* (Green Forest, Arkansas: Master Books, 2005). See also www.answersingenesis.org/go/helium.

[2] John D. Morris, Ph.D., *The Young Earth* (Green Forest, Arkansas: Master Books, 2007), 83–87. See also www.answersingenesis.org/creation/v21/i1/seas.asp.

Despite the claims of many scientists, if you examine the evidence objectively, it is obvious that evolution and millions of years have not been proven. You can be confident that if you teach that what the Bible says is true, you won't go wrong. Instill in your student a confidence in the truth of the Bible in all areas. If scientific thought seems to contradict the Bible, realize that scientists often make mistakes, but God does not lie. At one time scientists believed that the earth was the center of the universe, that living things could spring from non-living things, and that blood-letting was good for the body. All of these were believed to be scientific facts but have since been disproved, but the Word of God remains true. If we use modern "science" to interpret the Bible, what will happen to our faith in God's Word when scientists change their theories yet again?

INTEGRATING THE SEVEN C's INTO YOUR CURRICULUM

Throughout the *God's Design® for Science* series you will see icons that represent the Seven C's of History. The Seven C's is a framework in which all of history, and the future to come, can be placed. As we go through our daily routines we may not understand how the details of life connect with the truth that we find in the Bible. This is also the case for students. When discussing the importance of the Bible you may find yourself telling students that the Bible is relevant in everyday activities. But how do we help the younger generation see that? The Seven C's are intended to help.

The Seven C's can be used to develop a biblical worldview in students, young or old. Much more than entertaining stories and religious teachings, the Bible has real connections to our everyday life. It may be hard, at first, to see how many connections there are, but with practice, the daily relevance of God's Word will come alive. Let's look at the Seven C's of History and how each can be connected to what the students are learning.

CREATION

God perfectly created the heavens, the earth, and all that is in them in six normal-length days around 6,000 years ago.

This teaching is foundational to a biblical worldview and can be put into the context of any subject. In science, the amazing design that we see in nature—whether in the veins of a leaf or the complexity of your hand—is all the handiwork of God. Virtually all of the lessons in *God's Design for Science* can be related to God's creation of the heavens and earth.

Other contexts include:

Natural laws—any discussion of a law of nature naturally leads to God's creative power.

DNA and information—the information in every living thing was created by God's supreme intelligence.

Mathematics—the laws of mathematics reflect the order of the Creator.

Biological diversity—the distinct kinds of animals that we see were created during the Creation Week, not as products of evolution.

Art—the creativity of man is demonstrated through various art forms.

History—all time scales can be compared to the biblical time scale extending back about 6,000 years.

Ecology—God has called mankind to act as stewards over His creation.

CORRUPTION

After God completed His perfect creation, Adam disobeyed God by eating the forbidden fruit. As a result, sin and death entered the world, and the world has been in decay since that time. This point is evident throughout the world that we live in. The struggle for survival in animals, the death of loved ones, and the violence all around us are all examples of the corrupting influence of sin. Other contexts include:

Genetics—the mutations that lead to diseases, cancer, and variation within populations are the result of corruption.

Biological relationships—predators and parasites result from corruption.

History—wars and struggles between mankind, exemplified in the account of Cain and Abel, are a result of sin.

CATASTROPHE

God was grieved by the wickedness of mankind and judged this wickedness with a global Flood. The Flood covered the entire surface of the earth and killed all air-breathing creatures that were not aboard the Ark. The eight people and the animals aboard the Ark replenished the earth after God delivered them from the catastrophe.

The catastrophe described in the Bible would naturally leave behind much evidence. The studies of geology and of the biological diversity of animals on the planet are two of the most obvious applications of this event. Much of scientific understanding is based on how a scientist views the events of the Genesis Flood.

Other contexts include:

Biological diversity—all of the birds, mammals, and other air-breathing animals have populated the earth from the original kinds which left the Ark.

Geology—the layers of sedimentary rock seen in roadcuts, canyons, and other geologic features are testaments to the global Flood.

Geography—features like mountains, valleys, and plains were formed as the floodwaters receded.

Physics—rainbows are a perennial sign of God's faithfulness and His pledge to never flood the entire earth again.

Fossils—Most fossils are a result of the Flood rapidly burying plants and animals.

Plate tectonics—the rapid movement of the earth's plates likely accompanied the Flood.

Global warming/Ice Age—both of these items are likely a result of the activity of the Flood. The warming we are experiencing today has been present since the peak of the Ice Age (with variations over time).

CONFUSION

God commanded Noah and his descendants to spread across the earth. The refusal to obey this command and the building of the tower at Babel caused God to judge this sin. The common language of the people was confused and they spread across the globe as groups with a common language. All people are truly of "one blood" as descendants of Noah and, originally, Adam.

The confusion of the languages led people to scatter across the globe. As people settled in new areas, the traits they carried with them became concentrated in those populations. Traits like dark skin were beneficial in the tropics while other traits benefited populations in northern climates, and distinct people groups, not races, developed.

Other contexts include:

Genetics—the study of human DNA has shown that there is little difference in the genetic makeup of the so-called "races."

Languages—there are about seventy language groups from which all modern languages have developed.

Archaeology—the presence of common building structures, like pyramids, around the world confirms the biblical account.

Literature—recorded and oral records tell of similar events relating to the Flood and the dispersion at Babel.

CHRIST

God did not leave mankind without a way to be redeemed from its sinful state. The Law was given to Moses to show how far away man is from God's standard of perfection. Rather than the sacrifices, which only covered sins, people needed a Savior to take away their sin. This was accomplished when Jesus Christ came to earth to live a perfect life and, by that obedience, was able to be the sacrifice to satisfy God's wrath for all who believe.

The deity of Christ and the amazing plan that was set forth before the foundation of the earth is the core of Christian doctrine. The earthly life of Jesus was the fulfillment of many prophecies and confirms the truthfulness of the Bible. His miracles and presence in human form demonstrate that God is both intimately concerned with His creation and able to control it in an absolute way.

Other contexts include:

Psychology—popular secular psychology teaches of the inherent goodness of man, but Christ has lived the only perfect life. Mankind needs a Savior to redeem it from its unrighteousness.

Biology—Christ's virgin birth demonstrates God's sovereignty over nature.

Physics—turning the water into wine and the feeding of the five thousand demonstrate Christ's deity and His sovereignty over nature.

History—time is marked (in the western world) based on the birth of Christ despite current efforts to change the meaning.

Art—much art is based on the life of Christ and many of the masters are known for these depictions, whether on canvas or in music.

CROSS

Because God is perfectly just and holy, He must punish sin. The sinless life of Jesus Christ was offered as a substitutionary sacrifice for all of those who will repent and put their faith in the Savior. After His death on the Cross, He defeated death by rising on the third day and is now seated at the right hand of God.

The events surrounding the crucifixion and resurrection have a most significant place in the life of Christians. Though there is no way to scientifically prove the resurrection, there is likewise no way to prove the stories of evolutionary history. These are matters of faith founded in the truth of God's Word and His character. The eyewitness testimony of over 500 people and the written Word of God provide the basis for our belief.

Other contexts include:

Biology—the biological details of the crucifixion can be studied alongside the anatomy of the human body.

History—the use of crucifixion as a method of punishment was short-lived in historical terms and not known at the time it was prophesied.

Art—the crucifixion and resurrection have inspired many wonderful works of art.

CONSUMMATION

God, in His great mercy, has promised that He will restore the earth to its original state—a world without death, suffering, war, and disease. The corruption introduced by Adam's sin will be removed. Those who have repented and put their trust in the completed work of Christ on the Cross will experience life in this new heaven and earth. We will be able to enjoy and worship God forever in a perfect place.

This future event is a little more difficult to connect with academic subjects. However, the hope of a life in God's presence and in the absence of sin can be inserted in discussions of human conflict, disease, suffering, and sin in general.

Other contexts include:

History—in discussions of war or human conflict the coming age offers hope.

Biology—the violent struggle for life seen in the predator-prey relationships will no longer taint the earth.

Medicine—while we struggle to find cures for diseases and alleviate the suffering of those enduring the effects of the Curse, we ultimately place our hope in the healing that will come in the eternal state.

The preceding examples are given to provide ideas for integrating the Seven C's of History into a broad range of curriculum activities. We would recommend that you give your students, and yourself, a better understanding of the Seven C's framework by using AiG's Seven C's of History curriculum. The curriculum provides seven lessons that will establish a solid understanding of the true history, and future, of the universe. Full lesson plans, activities, and student resources are provided in the curriculum set.

We also offer bookmarks displaying the Seven C's and a wall chart. These can be used as visual cues for the students to help them recall the information and integrate new learning into its proper place in a biblical worldview.

Even if you use other curricula, you can still incorporate the Seven C's teaching into those. Using this approach will help students make firm connections between biblical events and every aspect of the world around them, and they will begin to develop a truly biblical worldview and not just add pieces of the Bible to what they learn in "the real world."

PROPERTIES OF ATOMS & MOLECULES

ATOMS & MOLECULES

ATOMS & MOLECULES

INTRODUCTION TO CHEMISTRY

THE STUDY OF MATTER AND MOLECULES

SUPPLY LIST

Drinking glass   Baking soda   Vinegar

Supplies for Challenge: 2-liter bottle of diet soda   Mentos® candies   Toothpick   Tape

Piece of paper

WHAT DID WE LEARN?

- What is matter? **Anything that has mass and takes up space.**

- Does air have mass? **Yes. It may seem like there is nothing there, but even though air is very light, it still has mass. The air contains molecules that take up space.**

- What do chemists study? **The way matter reacts with other matter and the environment.**

TAKING IT FURTHER

- Would you expect to see the same reaction each time you combine baking soda and vinegar? **Yes, because God designed certain laws for matter to follow, so we would expect it to react the same way each time.**

ATOMS

BASIC BUILDING BLOCKS

SUPPLY LIST

Copy of "Atomic Models" worksheet   Colored pencils

Supplies for Challenge: Copy of "Energy Levels" worksheet

ATOMIC MODELS WORKSHEET

- Color the protons in each atom red (white), the neutrons blue (black), and the electrons gray.

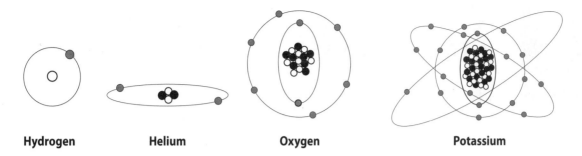

Hydrogen   **Helium**   **Oxygen**   **Potassium**

What did we learn?

- What is an atom? **The smallest part of matter that cannot be broken down by ordinary chemical means.**

- What are the three parts of an atom? **Protons, neutrons, and electrons**

- What electrical charge does each part of the atom have? **Protons are positive, neutrons are neutral, and electrons are negative.**

- What is the nucleus of an atom? **The dense center of the atom consisting of protons and neutrons.**

- What part of the atom determines what type of atom it is? **The number of protons in the nucleus determines what kind of atom it is.**

- What is a valence electron? **An electron in the outermost energy level for that atom.**

Taking it further

- Why is it necessary to use a model to show what an atom is like? **Atoms are too small to see and are very complex, so a model is useful for understanding what an atom is like.**

- On your worksheet, you colored neutrons blue and protons red. Are neutrons actually blue and protons actually red in a real atom? **No, the colors used in a model are just to help us visualize the parts. They do not really represent the actual colors.**

Challenge: Energy Levels worksheet

Element	Energy levels	Electrons in level 1	Electrons in level 2	Electrons in level 3	Electrons in level 4	Electrons in level 5	Electrons in level 6
He Helium	1	1					
Be Beryllium	2	2	2				
Al Aluminum	3	2	8	3			
Cl Chlorine	3	2	8	7			
Fe Iron	4	2	8	14	2		
Kr Krypton	4	2	8	18	8		
Ag Silver	5	2	8	18	18	1	
Au Gold	6	2	8	18	32	18	1

ATOMIC MASS

HOW BIG IS AN ATOM?

SUPPLY LIST

Copy of "Learning About Atoms" worksheet

Supplies for Challenge: Copy of "Understanding Atoms" worksheet

LEARNING ABOUT ATOMS WORKSHEET

Element	Atomic number	Atomic mass	# of of protons	# of electrons	# of neutrons
Hydrogen	1	1	1	1	0
Helium	2	4	2	2	2
Oxygen	8	16	8	8	8
Fluorine	9	19	9	9	10
Chromium	24	52	24	24	28

WHAT DID WE LEARN?

- What are the three particles that make up an atom? **Proton, electron, and neutron.**
- What is the atomic number of an atom? **The number of protons in the nucleus.**
- What is the atomic mass of an atom? **The sum of the protons and neutrons in the nucleus of the atom.**
- How can you determine the number of electrons, protons, and neutrons in an atom if you are given the atomic number and atomic mass? **The number of protons is the same as the atomic number. The number of electrons is equal to the number of protons. The number of neutrons is equal to the atomic mass minus the number of protons.**

TAKING IT FURTHER

- What does a hydrogen atom become if it loses its electron? **A proton.**
- Why are electrons ignored when calculating an element's mass? **The mass of an electron is so small compared to the mass of a proton or neutron that it does not make a significant difference.**

CHALLENGE: UNDERSTANDING ATOMS WORKSHEET

Element	Symbol	Atomic number	Atomic mass	# of protons	# of electrons	Most common # of neutrons
Hydrogen	**H**	1	1.008	1	1	0
Oxygen	**O**	8	16	8	8	8
Boron	**B**	5	10.81	5	5	6
Gold	**Au**	79	197	79	79	118
Silver	**Ag**	47	107.9	47	47	61
Uranium	**U**	92	238	92	92	146

Potassium	K	19	39.1	19	19	20
Chlorine	Cl	17	35.45	17	17	18
Neon	Ne	10	20.18	10	10	10
Einsteinium	Es	99	252	99	99	153

LESSON
4

MOLECULES

PUTTING ATOMS TOGETHER

SUPPLY LIST

Copy of "What Am I?" worksheet

Supplies for Challenge: Copy of "Molecule Puzzle Pieces"   Scissors

WHAT AM I? WORKSHEET

Next to each of the substances below, write whether it is an element, a diatomic molecule or a compound. Review these terms in the lesson if you need to.

Gold (Au): **Element**

Oxygen (O_2): **Diatomic molecule**

Silver (Ag): **Element**

Ammonia (NH_3): **Compound**

Nitrogen (N_2): **Diatomic molecule**

Salt (NaCl): **Compound**

WHAT DID WE LEARN?

• What is a molecule? **Two or more atoms chemically connected or bonded together.**

• What is a diatomic molecule? **A molecule with two of the same type of atoms connected together.**

• What is a compound? **A molecule made from two or more different kinds of atoms.**

TAKING IT FURTHER

• What is the most important factor in determining if two atoms will bond with each other? **The number of valence electrons each atom has.**

• Table salt is a compound formed from sodium and chlorine. Would you expect sodium atoms and chlorine atoms to taste salty? Why or why not? **No, because when molecules are formed, the resulting compound is a new substance with its own characteristics, completely different from those of the original elements.**

QUIZ 1 · ATOMS & MOLECULES

LESSONS 1–4

Label the parts of this helium atom.

A. _Electron_

B. _Proton or neutron_

C. _Neutron or proton_

B and C together form the _nucleus_.

Match the term with its definition.

1. _D_ Anything that has mass and takes up space

2. _E_ A positively charged particle in an atom

3. _I_ A negatively charged particle in an atom

4. _B_ A neutral particle in the nucleus

5. _A_ Mass of a proton or neutron

6. _J_ Compact center of the atom

7. _G_ Two atoms of the same element connected together

8. _F_ Part of matter that cannot be broken down chemically

9. _H_ Number of protons an element has

10. _C_ Two or more atoms chemically bonded

CHALLENGE QUESTIONS

11. Refer to the periodic table of the elements to complete the following chart.

Element	Atomic #	Atomic mass	# of protons	# of electrons	# of neutrons
Carbon	6	12.01	6	6	6
Aluminum	13	26.98	13	13	14
Tungsten	74	183.9	74	74	110

12. Based on the electron configurations for the following elements, which would not be likely to bond with any other elements? **Argon (Ar).**

13. What is an isotope? **An atom having the same number of protons but a different number of neutrons**.

14. What is a valence electron? **An electron in the outer shell of an atom**.

15. What is the electron configuration for silicon? **2, 8, 4.**

ELEMENTS

LESSON 5

THE PERIODIC TABLE OF THE ELEMENTS

ORGANIZING THE ELEMENTS

SUPPLY LIST

Copy of "Learning about the Elements" worksheet

LEARNING ABOUT THE ELEMENTS WORKSHEET

1. What is the symbol for calcium? **Ca.**
2. What is the symbol for silver? **Ag.**
3. What is the atomic number for copper? **29.**
4. What is the atomic mass for rutherfordium? **261.**
5. What are two elements in the same column as sodium? **H, Li, K, Rb, Cs, Fr.**
6. What are two elements with eight electrons in their outer layer? **Ne, Ar, Kr, Xe, Rn.**
7. How many electrons are in the outer layer of nitrogen? **5.**
8. How many layers of electrons does barium have? **6.**
9. Name one transition element. **Accept anything from columns IB–VIIB.**
10. Would silicon be more likely to react the same way as carbon or chlorine? **Carbon—they are in the same column and have the same number of valence electrons.**

WHAT DID WE LEARN?

- How many valence electrons do the elements in each column have? **Those in column IA have 1 valence electron; those in column IIA have 2, IIIA have 3, etc. Those in columns IB–VIIIB have 1 or 2 valence electrons.**

- What four pieces of information are included for each element in any Periodic Table of the Elements? **The element name, symbol, atomic number, and atomic mass.**

- What do all elements in a column on the periodic table have in common? **They have the same number of valence electrons.**

- What do all elements in a row on the periodic table have in common? **They have electrons in the same number of energy levels/same number of electron layers.**

TAKING IT FURTHER

- Atoms are stable when they have eight electrons in their outermost energy level. Therefore elements from column IA will react easily with elements from which column? **Column VIIA.**

- Elements from column IIA will react easily with elements from which column? **Column VIA.**

LESSON 6

METALS

SILVER AND GOLD HAVE I NONE . . .

SUPPLY LIST

Flashlight with battery   Electrical or duct tape   Copper wire

Supplies for Challenge: Copy of "Reactivity Series" worksheet

WHAT DID WE LEARN?

- What are the six characteristics of most metals? **Silvery luster, solid, malleable, ductile, conducts electricity, reacts with other elements.**

- How many valence electrons do most metals have? **Most commonly, metals have 1 or 2 valence electrons, but some have 3 or 4.**

- What is a metalloid? **An element that has some metal characteristics and some non-metal characteristics.**

TAKING IT FURTHER

- What are the most likely elements to be used in making computer chips? **The semiconductors—the ones shaded dark green on the periodic table of the elements. The most commonly used elements are silicon, germanium, and boron.**

- Is arsenic likely to be used as electrical wire in a house? **No, it is only a semi-conductor so it would not make good electrical wiring.**

CHALLENGE: REACTIVITY SERIES WORKSHEET

- **Most reactive to least reactive: Potassium, Sodium, Calcium, Magnesium, Aluminum, Zinc, Iron, Tin, Lead, Copper, Silver, Gold, Platinum.**

LESSON 7

NON-METALS

THE REST OF THE ELEMENTS

SUPPLY LIST

Eggs   Vinegar   Fluoride toothpaste   Nail polish or permanent marker

WHAT DID WE LEARN?

- What are some common characteristics of non-metals? **Not shiny or silver, not conductive, do not easily lose electrons.**

- What is the most common state, solid, liquid, or gas, for non-metal elements? **Gas.**

- Why are halogens very reactive? **They need only one electron to fill their outer shells.**

- Why are noble gases non-reactive? **They have a full outer shell of electrons.**

TAKING IT FURTHER

- Hydrogen often acts like a halogen. How might it act differently from a halogen? **Because hydrogen has only one electron, it can give up its electron and become an ion, whereas halogens do not easily give up electrons.**

- Why are balloons filled with helium instead of hydrogen? **Helium is a noble gas and non-reactive, but hydrogen is highly reactive. We don't want balloons exploding as the hydrogen reacts with another element.**

LESSON 8

HYDROGEN

VERY REACTIVE

SUPPLY LIST

Vegetable oil   Margarine   Peanut butter   Prepackaged food labels

WHAT DID WE LEARN?

- What is the most common element in the universe? **Hydrogen.**
- What is the atomic structure of hydrogen? **It has one proton and one electron.**
- What is the atomic number for hydrogen? **1.**
- What is the most common element in the universe? **Hydrogen**.
- Why is hydrogen sometimes grouped with the alkali metals? **It has only one electron so it often behaves like an alkali metal.**
- Why is hydrogen sometimes grouped with the halogens? **It is stable if it gains one electron so it often behaves like a halogen.**

TAKING IT FURTHER

- Why is hydrogen one of the most reactive elements? **Most elements must either gain electrons or lose electrons to combine with other elements. But hydrogen can do either one so it combines easily with many other elements.**

- Margarine contains only partially hydrogenated oil. What do you suppose fully hydrogenated oils are like? **They are much harder or more solid than margarine and are not easily spread.**

LESSON 9

CARBON

GRAPHITE AND DIAMONDS

SUPPLY LIST

Drawing paper   Colored pencils   Ceramic plate   Candle   Matches

WHAT DID WE LEARN?

- What is the atomic number and atomic structure of carbon? **Carbon is element number 6. It has 6 protons, 6 neutrons, and 6 electrons.**

- What makes a compound an organic compound? **It contains carbon atoms.**

- Name two common forms of carbon. **Graphite and diamond.**

- What is one by-product of burning coal? **Carbon dioxide.**

TAKING IT FURTHER

- How does the carbon cycle demonstrate God's care for His creation? **It allows carbon to be recycled and keeps life continuing on earth.**

- What is the most likely event that caused coal formation? **The Genesis Flood would have buried large amounts of plants under tons of mud and water. This is the most likely cause of the large amounts of coal found in the earth.**

- What would happen if bacteria and fungi did not convert carbon into carbon dioxide gas? **The carbon from dead plants and animals would become trapped and would not be able to be reused in the growth of new plants.**

LESSON 10

OXYGEN

A VERY ESSENTIAL ELEMENT

SUPPLY LIST

Candle   Small piece of dry ice   Matches   Gloves   Glass cup
Supplies for Challenge: Steel wool   2 test tubes   Small dish   Dish soap

WHAT DID WE LEARN?

- What is the atomic structure of oxygen? **Oxygen has 8 protons and 8 neutrons in the nucleus, and 8 electrons. It has 6 valence electrons.**

- How is ozone different from the oxygen we breathe? **Ozone is a molecule of three oxygen atoms. The oxygen we breathe is a molecule of two oxygen atoms. O_3 is poisonous and O_2 is not.**

TAKING IT FURTHER

- Why does the existence of ozone in the upper atmosphere show God's provision for life on earth? **If ozone were in the lower atmosphere, it would poison all living things. But in the upper atmosphere, it protects the earth from harmful radiation.**

- How do animals in the ocean get the needed oxygen to "burn" the food they eat? **Most aquatic animals have gills that extract oxygen from the water. A few, like whales and dolphins, have to surface and breathe air.**

- Why are oxygen atoms nearly always combined with other atoms? **They have only six valence electrons, so they are not stable by themselves.**

QUIZ 2 — ELEMENTS

LESSONS 5–10

Short answer:

1. What do elements in a column of the periodic table have in common? **The same number of valence electrons.**

2. What do elements in a row of the periodic table have in common? **Electrons filling the same energy levels.**

3. Which column of elements is most stable? **VIIIA.**

4. Elements in which column are most likely to react with elements in column VIA? **IIA.**

5. Elements in which column are most likely to react with elements in column VIIA? **IA.**

Write metal, metalloid, or non-metal to match the type of element to its characteristics.

6. _**Metal**_ Silvery luster

7. _**Metal**_ Ductile

8. _**Metal**_ Conducts electricity

9. _**Non-metal**_ Does not conduct electricity

10. _**Metal**_ Solid at room temperature

11. _**Non-metal**_ Not shiny

12. _**Metalloid**_ Somewhat malleable

13. _**Non-metal**_ Most often a gas

14. _**Metalloid**_ Semiconductor

15. _**Metal**_ Malleable

Mark each statement as either True or False.

16. _**T**_ Hydrogen is very reactive.

17. _**F**_ Oxygen is lighter than hydrogen.

18. _**T**_ Hydrogen is sometimes grouped with alkali metals.

19. _**T**_ Hydrogen is sometimes grouped with halogens.

20. _**F**_ Hydrogen is the most common element on earth.

21. _**T**_ All elements are recycled—they are not destroyed.

22. _**T**_ Carbon forms organic compounds.

CHALLENGE QUESTIONS

Match the term to its definition.

23. _**B**_ Column of the periodic table

24. _**F**_ Row of the periodic table

25. _**A**_ Metals in column 1

26. _**D**_ Metals in column 2

27. _**E**_ Non-reactive metals

28. _**G**_ Ball-shaped carbon molecule

29. _**H**_ Thread-like cylinders of carbon atoms

30. _**C**_ Technology that combines hydrogen and oxygen to produce electricity

UNIT 3
BONDING

LESSON
11

IONIC BONDING
GIVING UP ELECTRONS

SUPPLY LIST

Colored mini-marshmallows   Toothpicks   Glue

Supplies for Challenge: Copy of "Name that Ion" worksheet

WHAT DID WE LEARN?

- What is the main feature in an atom that determines how it will bond with other atoms? **The number of valence electrons it contains.**

- What kind of bond is formed when one atom gives up electrons and the other atom takes the electrons from it? **An ionic bond.**

- What is electronegativity? **A measure of how tightly an element holds on to its valence electrons.**

- Why are compounds that are formed when one element takes electrons from another called ionic compounds? **Because ions are formed when electrons are taken away or added.**

- What are some common characteristics of ionic compounds? **Conduct electricity when melted or dissolved, high melting point, soluble in water, brittle, form ions, form crystal lattices.**

- Which element has a higher electronegativity, chlorine or potassium? **Electronegativity increases as you go from left to right across the periodic table. Chlorine holds on to its electrons more tightly than potassium, so it has a higher electronegativity.**

TAKING IT FURTHER

- Which column of elements are the atoms in column IA most likely to form ionic bonds with? **The elements in column VIIA.**

- Use the Periodic Table of the Elements to determine the number of electrons that barium would give up in an ionic bond. **Barium has 2 valence electrons that it would give up.**

CHALLENGE: NAME THAT ION WORKSHEET

NaF: **Sodium fluoride**   KCl: **Potassium chloride**   CaCl2: **Calcium chloride or calcium dichloride**

LiBr: **Lithium bromide**   CaS: **Calcium sulfide**

LESSON 12

COVALENT BONDING

SHARING ELECTRONS

SUPPLY LIST

Colored mini-marshmallows   Toothpicks   Glue

Supplies for Challenge: Distilled water   9-volt battery   Copper wire   Sugar   Salt

Baking soda   Olive oil   4 paper cups   Copy of "Bonding Experiment" worksheet

WHAT DID WE LEARN?

- What is a covalent bond? **A bond formed when electrons are shared between two or more atoms.**

- What are some common characteristics of covalent compounds? **Do not conduct electricity, low melting point, strong, flexible, lightweight, insoluble in water, only slight attraction for each other.**

- What is the most common covalent compound on earth? **Water.**

TAKING IT FURTHER

- Why do diatomic molecules form covalent bonds instead of ionic bonds? **Diatomic molecules are formed from two atoms of the same element, so they have the same electronegativity. Since neither atom is able to take away or give up its electrons, they cannot form ionic bonds.**

- Would you expect more compounds to form ionic bonds or covalent bonds? **Since there are so many metals and only a few metalloids and non-metals, you might expect most compounds to be ionic. However, there are actually so many different ways to share electrons that covalent bonds are actually more common.**

CHALLENGE: BONDING EXPERIMENT WORKSHEET

- Use a periodic table to determine if each of the following compounds is composed of metals, non-metals, or both.

Water—H_2O is composed of _**non-metals**_

Baking Soda—$NaHCO_3$ is composed of _**both**_

Sugar (sucrose)—$C_{12}H_{22}O_{11}$ is composed of _**non-metals**_

Salt—$NaCl$ is composed of _**both**_

Olive oil—$C_{17}H_{35}COOH$ is composed of _**non-metals**_

Compound tested	Will it conduct electricity? (Hypothesis)	Did it conduct electricity? (Observations)	Ionic or covalent? (Conclusions)
Distilled water		**No**	**Covalent**
Baking soda		**Yes**	**Ionic**
Sugar		**No**	**Covalent**
Salt		**Yes**	**Ionic**
Olive oil		**No**	**Covalent**

LESSON 13

METALLIC BONDING

SHARING ON A LARGE SCALE

SUPPLY LIST

Colored mini-marshmallows   Toothpicks   Glue

Supplies for challenge: Copy of "Bonding Characteristics" worksheet

WHAT DID WE LEARN?

- What is the free electron theory? **It is the theory that metals form bonds by sharing electrons on a very large scale. Thousands of atoms allow their electrons to freely move about so that the atoms remain stable.**

- How many valence electrons do metals usually have? **Usually 1, 2, or 3.**

- What are common characteristics of metallic compounds? **Free electrons, conduct electricity and heat, shiny luster, high melting point, insoluble in water.**

TAKING IT FURTHER

- Why don't metals form ionic or covalent bonds? **Because they have similar numbers of valence electrons, they do not pull electrons away from each other. Also, because they have a low number of valence electrons, they do not have enough to share among a small number of atoms. Therefore, they must share on a large scale—among thousands of atoms.**

- Would you expect semiconductors to form metallic bonds? **No. Since they do not conduct electricity well, they would not have free electrons.**

CHALLENGE: BONDING CHARACTERISTICS WORKSHEET

Ionic bonding	Covalent bonding	Metallic bonding
A	C	B
F	D	D
G	H	I
J	K	J
L	M	L
O	N	N

LESSON 14

MINING & METAL ALLOYS

MAKING IT STRONGER

SUPPLY LIST

Tarnished silver object   Silver polish   Soft cloth

Supplies for Challenge: Copy of "Common Alloys" worksheet

WHAT DID WE LEARN?

- What element is combined with most metals to form metal ore? **Most metals are in the form of metal oxides—metals combined with oxygen.**

- What must be done to metal oxides to obtain pure metal? **The oxygen must be removed through a reduction reaction.**

- What is an alloy? **A metal that has a small amount of another metal added to it.**

- Why are alloys produced? **Alloys are often stronger, more resilient, and easier to work with than pure metals.**

TAKING IT FURTHER

- Do you think chromium would be added to steel that is going to be used in saw blades? Why or why not? **Probably not. Chromium keeps steel from oxidizing; however, a little oxidation on a saw blade will not keep it from working. The saw blade needs to be strong, so tungsten may be added, but not chromium.**

- Is oxidation of metal always a bad thing? **Not always. Sometimes a layer of oxidation prevents more oxygen from reaching the rest of the metal. So leaving a small amount of oxidation can actually reduce the overall amount of oxidation that occurs. This is not always the case, however; sometimes oxidation, such as rust, continues to occur until the sample is completely gone.**

CHALLENGE: COMMON ALLOYS WORKSHEET

Bronze: **Copper, tin**

Brass: **Copper, zinc**

Steel: **Iron, carbon**

Solder: **Tin, lead**

Duraluminium: **Aluminum, copper**

Magnalium: **Aluminum, magnesium**

Pewter: **Tin, copper, sometimes antimony or bismuth**

Sterling silver: **Silver and usually copper**

Stainless steel: **Iron, carbon, nickel, chromium**

LESSON 15

CRYSTALS

SPARKLING LIKE DIAMONDS

SUPPLY LIST

Table salt   2 plates   Epsom salt   Scissors   Dark construction paper   Small pan
Optional activity: geode
Supplies for Challenge: Plaster of Paris   Modeling clay

WHAT DID WE LEARN?

- What is a crystal? **A substance whose atoms are lined up in a regular lattice configuration. Crystals have smooth faces and defined edges.**

- How do crystals form? **When a liquid cools slowly, the atoms line up in regular patterns to form crystal lattices based on their chemical characteristics.**

- What is an artificial gem? **One that is formed by man and not formed naturally.**

- Where would you look to find crystals? **In rocks and minerals, in the kitchen (salt and sugar), in caves, jewelry.**

TAKING IT FURTHER

- Why are naturally occurring gems more valuable than artificial gems when many are made from the same materials? **Even though they are made from the same materials, artificial gems do not have the same strength and brilliance of naturally occurring crystals. God's crystals are still better than man's.**

- Why is a saturated solution better for forming crystals? **The more atoms of the crystal forming material you have, such as salt, the more likely they are to line up in a lattice formation.**

- What are some ways you use crystals in your home? **In food, in your computer, TV, phone, and other electronic devices, in your rock collection, gems in your mother's wedding ring, etc.**

LESSON

16

CERAMICS

MAKING IT WITH CLAY

SUPPLY LIST

Polymer clay (Femo, Sculpey, etc.)

WHAT DID WE LEARN?

- What is ceramic? **It is a material that is formed when ingredients fuse together by heat; often made with clay.**

- What are some examples of traditional ceramics? **Pottery, brick, porcelain, and glass.**

- What makes ceramics hard? **The material forms crystals when it is baked or fired.**

- What are some advantages of modern ceramics? **They are hard, strong, heat resistant, and don't rust.**

TAKING IT FURTHER

- Why are the tiles on the space shuttle made of ceramic? **Because ceramic is very heat resistant, the tiles keep the heat generated by friction with the atmosphere away from the shuttle, allowing the shuttle to reenter the atmosphere without burning up.**

- Why are crystalline structures stronger than non-crystalline structures? **The lattice shape of the bonds allows atoms to be connected in more than one direction, so the compounds are stronger.**

QUIZ

3

BONDING

LESSONS 11–16

For each characteristic below, write I if it describes an ionic bond, C for a covalent bond, and M for a metallic bond. Some characteristics have more than one answer.

1. _I_ Formed by elements with very different levels of electronegativity

2. _I,M_ High melting point

3. _C_ Electrons are shared between two or three atoms

4. _C,M_ Insoluble in water

5. _I_ Forms ions

6. _I_ Electrons are given up or pulled away

7. _C_ Does not conduct electricity

8. _M_ Sharing of electrons on a large scale

9. _I,M_ Conducts electricity

10. _C_ Flexible

Short answer:

11. How are crystals formed? **When a liquid slowly cools the atoms may line up in specific patterns to form crystals.**

12. What is the smooth side of a crystal called? **A face.**

13. What process is necessary for ceramics to become strong? **Heating or firing.**

14. What is the common ingredient in all natural ceramics? **Clay.**

15. Name three traditional ceramics. **Pottery, brick, porcelain, glass.**

CHALLENGE QUESTIONS

Mark each statement as either True or False.

16. _T_ Ionic bonding occurs between elements with very different electronegativities.

17. _F_ Ions are electrically neutral.

18. _F_ Ionic bonds occur between non-metals.

19. _T_ Sodium fluoride is an ionic compound.

20. _F_ Covalent compounds easily conduct electricity.

21. _T_ Covalent bonds occur between non-metals.

22. _F_ Metallic materials easily dissolve in water.

23. _T_ Metallic bonds have free electrons.

24. _T_ Metallic bonds form between elements with similar low electronegativities.

25. _T_ Brass is an alloy of copper and zinc.

26. _F_ Steel is an allow of copper and tin.

27. _F_ Hydrates usually feel wet.

28. _T_ Hydrates can help prevent the spread of fire.

29. _T_ Resorbable ceramics are absorbed into the body.

30. _F_ Inert ceramics react with the body.

CHEMICAL REACTIONS

LESSON 17

CHEMICAL REACTIONS

CHANGING FROM ONE THING TO ANOTHER

SUPPLY LIST

Birthday candle　　Vinegar　　Modeling clay　　Baking soda　　Jar　　Matches
Supplies for Challenge: 6 clear cups　　6 Alka-Seltzer tablets　　Water　　Ice　　Spoon
Stopwatch　　Copy of "Reaction Rate Experiment" worksheet

WHAT DID WE LEARN?

- What is a chemical reaction? **When atomic bonds are formed or broken—when two or more elements combine together to form a new substance, or when a substance is broken down into its separate elements.**

- What are the initial ingredients in a chemical reaction called? **Reactants.**

- What are the resulting substances of a chemical reaction called? **Products.**

TAKING IT FURTHER

- How might you speed up a chemical reaction? **Add heat; add surface area to the reactants by changing their shape—make them thinner or break or crush them; increase the concentration of the reactants; add a catalyst.**

- A fire hose usually sprays water on a fire to put it out. Water does not deprive the fire of oxygen, so why does water put out a fire? **Water absorbs the heat from the fire, and heat is another necessary ingredient in producing and sustaining a fire.**

- What chemical reaction do you think is taking place in the making of a loaf of bread? **The yeast reacts with the sugar in the bread dough to produce carbon dioxide.**

CHALLENGE: REACTION RATE EXPERIMENT WORKSHEET

- **You should see the tablet in the hot water dissolve more quickly than the tablets in the other cups. You should see the crushed tablet dissolve more quickly than th tablets in the other cups.**

CHEMICAL EQUATIONS

DESCRIBING HOW IT WORKS

SUPPLY LIST

Copy of "Understanding Chemical Equations" worksheet

Supplies for Challenge: Copy of "Reactants and Products" worksheet

UNDERSTANDING CHEMICAL EQUATIONS WORKSHEET

1. $C + O_2 \longrightarrow CO_2$
2. $N_2 + 3H_2 \longrightarrow 2NH_3$
3. $2H_2O \longrightarrow 2H_2 + O_2$

WHAT DID WE LEARN?

*   What is a chemical equation? **It is an equation that visually shows what happens to each element in a chemical reaction.**
*   What are the elements or compounds on the left side of a chemical equation called? **The reactants.**
*   What are the elements or compounds on the right side of a chemical equation called? **The products.**

TAKING IT FURTHER

*   Why is it helpful to use chemical equations? **Equations provide a visual way to see what is happening in a chemical reaction without drawing pictures.**

CHALLENGE: REACTANTS & PRODUCTS WORKSHEET

1. $4\,Al + 3O_2 \longrightarrow$ _B_
2. $H_2SO_4 + 2\,LiOH \longrightarrow$ _A_
3. $4\,NH_3 + 3\,O_2 \longrightarrow$ _C_
4. $P_4 + 10\,Cl_2 \longrightarrow$ _E_
5. $CO_2 \longrightarrow$ _D_
6. $H + OH \longrightarrow$ _F_
7. $2\,KClO_3 \longrightarrow$ _H_
8. $2\,Na + 2\,H_2O \longrightarrow$ _G_
*   Which of the above equations represent decomposition reactions? _ **5, 7** _
*   Which of the above equations represent composition reactions? _ **1, 4, 6** _
*   Which of the above equations represent single displacement reactions? _ **3, 8** _
*   Which of the above equations represent double displacement reactions? _ **2** _

LESSON 19

CATALYSTS

SPEEDING THINGS UP

SUPPLY LIST

Potato   Hydrogen peroxide   Apple   Lemon juice

WHAT DID WE LEARN?

- What is a catalyst? **A substance added to speed up a chemical reaction.**
- How does a catalyst work? **It reduces the amount of energy needed for the chemical reaction to take place.**
- What is an inhibitor? **A substance that slows down or prevents a chemical reaction.**
- What is an enzyme? **A catalyst found in living cells.**

TAKING IT FURTHER

- Why is it important that living cells have enzymes? **If enzymes were not available, many chemical reactions such as digestion would take much too long to occur.**
- Are catalysts always good? **Not necessarily. If a catalyst caused food to spoil very quickly that would be a bad use of a catalyst.**

LESSON 20

ENDOTHERMIC & EXOTHERMIC REACTIONS

WHAT HAPPENS TO THE HEAT?

SUPPLY LIST

5 eggs   Vinegar (room temperature)   Small pan   Thermometer   Timer
Steel wool (no soap)   Jar with lid (Thermometer must fit inside the jar with the lid on)
Supplies for Challenge: Alka-Seltzer tablets   Thermometer   Styrofoam cup
Water   Copy of "Endothermic or Exothermic?" worksheet   Stopwatch

WHAT DID WE LEARN?

- What is an exothermic reaction? **A chemical reaction that releases energy.**
- What is an endothermic reaction? **A chemical reaction that absorbs energy.**

TAKING IT FURTHER

- If a chemical reaction produces a spark, is it likely to be an endothermic or exothermic reaction? **Light is a form of energy, so it would be an exothermic reaction.**
- How does photosynthesis and digestion reveal God's plan for life? **Photosynthesis absorbs and stores energy from the sun in the sugar molecules in the plant. That energy is released during digestion after an animal eats the plant. This is God's plan for providing necessary food, and therefore energy, for all of the animals—and humans—on earth.**

- If the temperature of the product is lower than the temperature of the reactants, was the reaction endothermic or exothermic? **If the result is cooler than the beginning reactants, then energy was absorbed, so the reaction was endothermic.**

CHALLENGE: ENDOTHERMIC OR EXOTHERMIC? WORKSHEET

- **The results should show the reaction is endothermic; the temperature of the water goes down during the reaction then levels off.**

QUIZ 4 CHEMICAL REACTIONS

LESSONS 17–20

Mark each statement as either True or False.

1. _F_ All chemical reactions are fast.
2. _T_ A catalyst speeds up a chemical reaction.
3. _T_ Endothermic reactions use up heat.
4. _F_ A fireworks explosion is an endothermic reaction.
5. _T_ The same number of atoms must appear on both sides of a chemical equation.
6. _T_ Chemical equations demonstrate the first law of thermodynamics.
7. _T_ Reactants are on the left side of a chemical equation.
8. _F_ Catalysts are used up in a chemical reaction.
9. _F_ Inhibitors speed up a chemical reaction.
10. _T_ Sometimes inhibitors are helpful.
11. _T_ Catalysts lower the energy required for a chemical reaction to occur.
12. _T_ Exothermic reactions release energy.
13. _F_ The product of an exothermic reaction is cooler than the reactants.
14. _F_ Chemical reactions are rare.
15. _T_ Heat can increase the reaction rate.

CHALLENGE QUESTIONS

16. _Double displacement_ $H_2SO_4 + 2\ LiOH \longrightarrow Li_2SO_4 + 2\ H_2O$
17. _Composition_ $P_4 + 10\ Cl_2 \longrightarrow 4\ PCl_5$
18. _Decomposition_ $CO_2 \longrightarrow C + O_2$
19. _Single displacement_ $2\ Na + 2\ H_2O \longrightarrow H_2 + 2\ NaOH$
20. _Double displacement_ $AgNo_3 + HCl \longrightarrow AgCl + HNO_3$

Short answer:

21. List three ways to increase the reaction rate of a chemical reaction: **Add heat, increase surface area of reactants, increase concentration of reactants, add a catalyst, reduce activation energy.**

22. List two groups of catalysts. **Heterogeneous, homogeneous.**

23. Which type of catalyst is found in a catalytic converter? **Heterogeneous.**

24. Which type of catalyst will bond with a reactant? **Homogeneous.**

25. What is the name for the energy stored in chemical bonds? **Enthalpy.**

ACIDS & BASES

LESSON 21

CHEMICAL ANALYSIS

WHAT IS IT MADE OF?

SUPPLY LIST

Red or purple cabbage   Pan or microwavable bowl

Supplies for Challenge: Research materials on chemical analysis

WHAT DID WE LEARN?

- What is chemical analysis? **Using chemical reactions to determine the composition of a substance.**
- List three different types of chemical analysis. **Flame test, spectrometer, indicators.**
- What is a chemical indicator? **A substance that changes color when it reacts with a specific chemical.**
- What is the pH scale? **The scale used to measure the strength of an acid or a base.**
- What does a pH of 7 tell you about the substance? **It is neutral. It is not an acid or a base.**

TAKING IT FURTHER

- Why is it important to periodically test the pH of swimming pool water? **Water must be close to neutral to be safe to swim in. Also, water with a pH much greater than 6.8–7.0 can cause pipes to become clogged with minerals.**
- Name at least one other use for testing pH of a liquid? **Hair treatments like permanents must be tested for pH so that hair curls and doesn't burn. Urine can be tested for pH to detect health problems. Beverages are tested for proper pH to ensure proper taste. Drinking water is tested for proper pH, and wastewater is tested before releasing it back into the water system.**

LESSON 22

ACIDS

DOES IT BURN?

SUPPLY LIST

Lemon juice   Vinegar   Lemon lime soda   Milk   Cabbage indicator from lesson 21

Supplies for Challenge: Jar with a lid   15 pennies   1 steel paper clip   Salt   Vinegar

TESTING FOR ACIDS

- **Lemon juice, vinegar, and soda pop should be acids. Saliva should be slightly acidic; milk should not be an acid.**

WHAT DID WE LEARN?

- What defines a substance as an acid? **It produces hydronium ions when dissolved in water.**
- What is a hydronium ion? **H_3O^+, formed by a water molecule and a hydrogen ion.**
- How is a weak acid different from a strong acid? **A weak acid holds onto its hydrogen atoms more strongly than a strong acid, so it forms fewer hydronium ions in water.**
- What are some common characteristics of an acid? **Sour taste, conducts electricity in water, reacts with metals, many are corrosive, neutralizes bases, reacts with indicators.**
- How can you tell if a substance is an acid? **Dissolve it in water and use an indicator to test for acid.**

TAKING IT FURTHER

- Why is saliva slightly acidic? **The acid in your saliva helps begin the digestion process by helping break down the food molecules.**
- Would you expect water taken from a puddle on the forest floor to be acidic, neutral, or basic? Why? **It would probably be acidic because the forest floor is covered with decaying plants, and decaying plants produce humic acid.**
- What would you expect to be a key ingredient in sour candy? **Some kind of acid. Sour spray and other sour candies often contain several types of acids.**

LESSON 23 BASES

THE OPPOSITE OF ACIDS

SUPPLY LIST

Ammonia (clear)   Soap   Anti-acid tablets or liquid   Baking soda   Toothpaste
Cabbage indicator from lesson 21

Supplies for Challenge: Ammonia   Eyedropper   Distilled water   Measuring cup
Measuring spoon   Clear glass   Vinegar   Cabbage indicator

TESTING FOR BASES

- **They should all be bases. However, if you tested liquid soap and the indicator showed it to be an acid or to be neutral, check the bottle to see if it contains some kind of citric acid, which is sometimes added for scent.**

WHAT DID WE LEARN?

- What defines a substance as a base? **It produces hydroxide ions when dissolved in water.**
- What is a hydroxide ion? **OH^- ion.**
- How is a weak base different from a strong base? **A weak base holds onto its hydroxide ions more strongly than a strong base does.**
- What are some common characteristics of a base? **Bitter taste, conducts electricity in water, feels slippery, many are corrosive, neutralizes acids, reacts with indicators.**

- How can you tell if a substance is a base? **Dissolve it in water and use an indicator to test for base.**

TAKING IT FURTHER

- If you spill a base, what should you do before trying to clean it up? **Add an acid to neutralize it.**
- Do you think that Strontium is likely to form a strong base? Why or why not? **Strontium is in the alkali metal family and alkali metals tend to form strong bases. Therefore, strontium is likely to form a strong base.**

LESSON 24

SALTS

PASS THE SALT, PLEASE.

SUPPLY LIST

Lemon juice   Anti-acid (tablet or liquid)   Table salt   Swabs
Supplies for Challenge: Copy of "Acid/Base Reactions" worksheet

WHAT DID WE LEARN?

- Did you detect the various flavors in the areas indicated on the above tongue map? **Answers may vary.**
- How is a salt formed? **When a negative acid ion combines with a positive base ion, a salt is formed.**
- What are two common characteristics of salts? **They have a salty flavor, and they form crystals.**
- How are salt families named? **By the acid from which they are made.**
- Name three salt families. **Sulfates, chlorides, nitrates, carbonates, phosphates, potash.**

TAKING IT FURTHER

- What do you expect to be the results of combining vinegar and lye? **You would get a salt and water.**
- Why are some salts still acidic or basic? **The ions do not completely combine together, so some hydrogen or hydroxide ions are still present.**
- If your tongue can only detect four different flavors, how can foods and drinks have so many different flavors? **There are many different combinations of acids, bases, salts, and sugars in foods so there is a great variety. Also, flavor is not just what you taste on your tongue. It also includes the smell of the food as well.**

CHALLENGE: ACID/BASE REACTIONS WORKSHEET

1. $HClO_3 + KOH \longrightarrow KClO_3 + H_2O$
    The acid is __HClO3__   The base is __KOH__   The salt is __KClO_3__
2. $HBr + Ca(OH)_2 \longrightarrow CaBr_2 + H_2O$
    The acid is __HBr__   The base is __Ca(OH)_2__   The salt is __CaBr_2__
3. $H_2SO_4 + 2NH_3 \longrightarrow 2NH_4^+ + SO_4^{2-}$
    The acid is __H_2SO_4__   The base is __NH_3__
4. $HI + H_2O \longrightarrow H_3O^+ + I^-$
    The acid is __HI__   The base is __H_2O__

Choose the best answer for each question.

1. _D_ Which is not a type of chemical analysis?

2. _A_ pH indicators can tell the strength of which type of compound?

3. _B_ What flower can indicate the pH of the soil by the color of its flowers?

4. _C_ Which of the following is not an acid?

5. _A_ Which of the following is not a base?

6. _A_ What is formed when an acid combines with a base?

7. _B_ Which is not a characteristic of acids?

8. _A_ Which is not a characteristic of bases?

9. _A_ Which acid is the most produced chemical in the United States?

10. _C_ What common product is made primarily from salts?

CHALLENGE QUESTIONS

Choose the best answer for each statement.

11. _C_ Electroplating is depositing a thin layer of metal on a **_conductor_**.

12. _A_ Titration allows you to calculate how many **_molecules_** are in an unknown sample.

13. _B_ A proton donor is another name for a(n) **_acid_**.

14. _C_ A proton acceptor is another name for a(n) **_base_**.

15. _D_ You can identify the acid in an equation because it loses a(n) **_hydrogen_** atom.

UNIT 6
BIOCHEMISTRY

LESSON
25

BIOCHEMISTRY

THE CHEMISTRY OF LIFE

SUPPLY LIST

Whatever food you have in your kitchen

Supplies for Challenge: Box of gelatin mix   Fresh pineapple juice   Vinegar   4 marbles
4 tall narrow cups   Measuring spoon   Copy of "Enzyme Reaction Rates" worksheet

WHAT DID WE LEARN?

- List at least two chemical functions performed inside living creatures. **Photosynthesis and digestion, or oxygen combining with hemoglobin. In plants, the equivalent of digestion is called internal or cellular respiration.**

- What is the chemical reaction that takes place during photosynthesis? **Water and carbon dioxide chemically combine to form sugar and oxygen.**

- What is the main chemical reaction that takes place during digestion? **Sugar and oxygen chemically combine to form carbon dioxide and water; also larger molecules are broken down into smaller molecules.**

- What substance is necessary for nearly every chemical reaction in living things? **Water.**

- Name the three major chemicals your body needs that are found in the foods we eat. **Proteins, fats, and carbohydrates.**

TAKING IT FURTHER

- Why did God design your body to have enzymes? **Enzymes help digestion and other metabolic processes to occur at a much quicker rate than they otherwise would.**

- With what you know about chemical processes, why do you think it is important to brush your teeth after you eat? **The chemicals in your mouth begin the digestion process. These chemicals can cause tooth decay if they stay in your mouth too long. So you need to brush away any food and acids so your teeth stay healthy.**

- Can you think of other chemical processes in your body besides the ones mentioned in this lesson? **Chemicals called hormones control your growth; chemicals are released to make you feel sleepy at bedtime; taste and smell are chemical reactions. These are just a few examples. The list of chemical reactions in your body is very long!**

CHALLENGE: ENZYME REACTION RATES WORKSHEET

1. What effects did the plain pineapple juice have on the gelatin? **The plain pineapple juice should break down the protein in the gelatin, allowing the marble to move down into the gelatin.**

2. What effects did heating the juice have on the way the juice affected the gelatin? **The heated juice should be less effective, allowing the marble to move more slowly.**

3. What effects did changing the pH have on the way the juice affected the gelatin? **Similarly, the vinegar changes the pH and makes the protease less effective, so the marble moves more slowly.**

4. Why was cup 4 necessary? **Cup 4 is a control; it shows that the movement of the marbles is due to the juice that was added and not just due to gravity.**

LESSON 26

DECOMPOSERS

ULTIMATE RECYCLING

SUPPLY LIST

Paper   Colored pencils

Supplies for Challenge: Banana   3 Plastic zipper bags   Baking yeast   Marker

Copy of "Rate of Decomposition" worksheet

WHAT DID WE LEARN?

- What is a scavenger? **An animal that eats dead animals.**

- What is a decomposer? **An organism that breaks down dead plants, dead animals or dung into simple chemical compounds.**

- What is this way of recycling nitrogen called? **The nitrogen cycle.**

TAKING IT FURTHER

- Why are decomposers necessary? **They are needed to break down complex compounds into simple compounds that can be used by plants. Without decomposers, the elements would be locked up and plants would not be able to grow.**

- Were there animal scavengers in God's perfect creation, before the Fall of man? **No, there was no animal or human death before Adam sinned. Man and animals were all created to be vegetarians—see Genesis 1:27-31.**

- Explain how a compost pile allows you to participate in the nitrogen cycle. **You can take food scraps, such as potato peels, and place them in a bin or pile outside. Bacteria or other decomposers eat these scraps, leaving behind compost, which is nutrient rich material that you can add to your garden. You have taken nitrogen from the food scraps and returned it to the soil to be used by the plants you grow in your garden.**

LESSON 27

CHEMICALS IN FARMING

HELPING PLANTS GROW

SUPPLY LIST

2 identical plants—a fast growing plant like mint is a good choice   Plant food or fertilizer

WHAT DID WE LEARN?

- What are three ways that farmers ensure their soil will have enough nutrients for their crops? **Adding fertilizers, allowing the land to lie fallow, crop rotation, burning of unwanted plants.**

- What is hydroponics? **Growing plants without soil, using chemicals in water.**

- How are chemicals used in farming other than for nutrients for the plants? **Chemicals are used to kill pests, diseases, and unwanted plants—pesticides, fungicides, and herbicides.**

- How is an organic farm different from other farms? **Organic farms do not use man-made chemicals.**

TAKING IT FURTHER

- Why did the farmers let cattle graze on their land once every fourth year in the Norfolk 4-course plant rotation method? **The animal waste added nutrients back into the soil.**

- How does hydroponics replace the role of soil in plant growth? **A framework is provided to support the plants, and nutrients are added to the water for absorption by the roots.**

LESSON 28 MEDICINES

HOW CHEMICAL COMPOUNDS AFFECT YOUR BODY

SUPPLY LIST

Bread   Butter or margarine   Garlic powder   Ginger ale

WHAT DID WE LEARN?

- Why are chemicals used as medicines? **Your body is constantly performing chemical reactions, so adding chemicals to your body causes different reactions to occur.**

- What were the earliest recorded medicines? **Herbs.**

- What was Sir Alexander Fleming's important discovery? **Penicillin—the first antibiotic.**

TAKING IT FURTHER

- If plants have the potential of supplying new medicines, where might a person look to find different plants? **One of the likeliest sources of medicinal plants is believed to be the tropical rainforests where there are thousands of unusual plants.**

- What other sources might there be for discovering new medicines? **In addition to plants, animals in the rainforest and ocean are likely places to test for new medicines. Also, a better understanding of how the human body processes chemicals can lead to the development of new synthetic medicines.**

QUIZ 6

BIOCHEMISTRY

LESSONS 25–28

Short answer:

1. Identify two chemical reactions that sustain life. **Photosynthesis, digestion.**
2. Name three main chemical compounds in food. **Carbohydrates, proteins, fat.**
3. What type of catalyst increases the rate of digestion processes? **Enzymes.**
4. What is an animal called that eats dead animals? **Decomposer or scavenger.**
5. Name two types of decomposers. **Bacteria, fungi.**
6. Name an element that is recycled by decomposers. **Nitrogen.**
7. Name three ways to keep farmland productive. **Crop rotation, lying fallow, fertilizers.**
8. Who was the discoverer of penicillin? **Alexander Fleming.**

Match the term with its definition.

9. _B_ Kills unwanted insects
10. _D_ Kills unwanted plants
11. _H_ Kills unwanted fungus
12. _C_ Farming without man-made chemicals
13. _A_ Growing plants without soil
14. _E_ Medicine to kill bacteria
15. _F_ Medicine to encourage natural defenses
16. _G_ Some of these plants have natural medicinal value

CHALLENGE QUESTIONS

Short answer:

17. What are two conditions that inhibit enzyme reaction rate? **Heat and decreased pH (increased acidity).**
18. What condition most promotes decomposition? **Darkness and/or warmth.**
19. What are two controversies surrounding organic farming? **Are organic foods healthier? Can organic farms produce as much as non-organic farms? Can organic farms really control pests? Are GMOs bad for us? Is organic farming better for the environment?**
20. Briefly explain how chemotherapy works to treat cancer. **The chemicals target reproducing cells and prevent them from completing reproduction, thus killing the cells. Cancer cells are quickly reproducing so are killed faster than other cells.**

UNIT 7
APPLICATIONS OF CHEMISTRY

LESSON 29

PERFUMES

WHAT'S THAT SMELL?

SUPPLY LIST

Jar with a lid   Rubbing alcohol   15 whole cloves

Supplies for Challenge: (several of the following) Ginger root   Mint leaves   Peppermint oil
Cinnamon sticks   Dried fruit   Flower petals   Allspice   Almond extract   Vanilla extract

WHAT DID WE LEARN?

- What is a perfume? **A liquid with a pleasing smell.**
- What must be removed from flower petals to make perfume? **The fragrant oil.**
- Describe the two main methods for removing oil from flower petals. **With solvent extraction, a solvent is used to dissolve the oils, then the solvent is allowed to evaporate. With steam distillation, steam is used to vaporize the oil, then both the oil and water condense and the oil is skimmed off the top of the water.**

TAKING IT FURTHER

- Why should you test a new perfume on your skin before you buy it? **The scent of the perfume in the bottle may not be the same as it is on your skin. The alcohol in the bottle may mask the true scent. So put some on your skin and see how it smells once the alcohol has evaporated.**
- Why wasn't it necessary to use one of the methods described in the lesson to make your homemade perfume? **As the cloves soaked in the alcohol, the scent particles slowly moved into the alcohol from the cloves. This is a very slow process. The methods described in the lesson greatly speed up the process for commercial production of perfume.**

LESSON 30

RUBBER

DO YOU HAVE A RUBBER BAND?

SUPPLY LIST

Balloon   Rubber band   Permanent marker

ATOMS & MOLECULES

What did we learn?

- What is natural rubber made from? **Latex from a rubber tree.**
- What is synthetic rubber made from? **Petroleum—oil.**
- What is vulcanization? **The process of adding sulfur to rubber to make it elastic in all types of weather.**
- What is a polymer? **A long chain of molecules connected together.**

Taking it further

- Why is it difficult to recycle automobile tires? **The vulcanization process makes the rubber very long lasting, but it also makes it hard to break down the molecules so recycling is difficult.**
- What advantages and disadvantages are there to using synthetic rubber instead of natural rubber? **Synthetic rubber is cheaper than natural rubber; however, it requires petroleum, much of which America must import from other countries.**

LESSON 31

PLASTICS

THE WONDER MATERIAL

SUPPLY LIST

Copy of "Chemical Word Search"

Supplies for Challenge: Borax   White glue   Cornstarch   Markers

CHEMICAL WORD SEARCH

```
S A L T V U K A T M A T O M E
C S T R I S Y N T H E T I C I
C P E R F U M E O R E A D F U
A E S S A K T V I X Y J I D Y
R P H O T O S Y N T H E S I S
B L R P S B O N D I U W T G Z
O A G O W T H E I S C N I E M
H S U L T B N M C D F H L S I
Y T V Y N E W B A S E B L T Z
D I S M Q U I I T A T T A I S
R C R E J E P N O B L I T O M
A R K R E B B U R C A L I N Y
T V U L C A N I Z A T I O N S
E A A C I D D H G Y T R N Y O
W P R U F R E S O P M O C E D
```

WHAT DID WE LEARN?

- What is plastic? **A substance made from polymers that are derived from petroleum.**
- What was celluloid, the first artificial polymer, made from? **From cellulose that comes from cotton plants.**

- What is the difference between thermoplastic and thermosetting resin? **Thermoplastics will become soft when reheated, thermosetting resin plastic will not.**

Taking it further

- Name three ways that plastic is used in sports. **Plastic or vinyl balls, artificial rubber soles on running shoes, plastic hooks to hold soccer nets in place, polyester sports clothes, and many other uses.**
- What advantages do plastic items have over natural materials? **Many plastic items are stronger, more flexible, and longer lasting than their natural counterparts.**

LESSON 32 FIREWORKS

Is it the Fourth of July?

Supply list

Construction paper or tagboard   Various colors of glitter   Glue
Supplies for Challenge: Epsom salts (found in the medicine section of the store)
Potassium chloride (used as a salt substitute-may be found in the spice section of grocery store)
Several pinecones   Borax and calcium chloride (may be found with laundry/cleaning supplies)
Copper sulfate (found where swimming pool supplies are sold)   Table salt
Several containers in which to soak the pinecones

What did we learn?

- What are the key ingredients in a fireworks shell? **The chemical that releases the light, black powder for the explosion, and fuses to light the powder.**
- Why does a fireworks shell have two different black powder charges? **One charge lifts the shell into the air and the other charge blasts the shell open.**
- How do fireworks generate flashes of light? **When the blasting charge explodes, the energy released forces electrons in the chemicals into higher energy levels. When the electrons return to their normal energy levels, they release energy in the form of light.**
- What determines the color of the firework? **The chemical compound that is packed inside.**

Taking it further

- How can a firework explode with one color and then change to a different color? **Two different chemicals are packed in the shell and ignited at different times.**
- Why would employees at a fireworks plant have to wear only cotton clothing? **Nylon, polyester, silk, and other fabrics can build up a static charge. This could be very dangerous when working around black powder because a static discharge could ignite the powder.**

LESSON 33
ROCKET FUEL

DO YOU NEED A ROCKET SCIENTIST?

SUPPLY LIST

Balloon   String   Soda straw   Tape

WHAT DID WE LEARN?

- What is combustion? **A chemical reaction that produces great amounts of heat.**
- What two elements are combined in most modern rocket fuel? **Oxygen and hydrogen.**
- What compound is produced in this reaction? **Water/steam.**
- How does combining oxygen and hydrogen produce lift? **The reaction takes place at very high temperatures—heating the atoms to very high temperatures and thus very high speeds. These molecules exit the engine at great speeds, thus producing lift because of Newton's third law of motion.**
- What is Newton's Third Law of Motion? **For every action there is an equal and opposite reaction.**

TAKING IT FURTHER

- Why is oxygen and hydrogen a better choice for rocket fuel than kerosene was? **The end product of the reaction of oxygen and hydrogen is steam, and the end product of kerosene combustion is carbon dioxide. Water is lighter than carbon dioxide so it can move faster. The faster the molecules are moving when they leave the rocket engine, the more lift they produce.**

QUIZ 7
APPLICATIONS OF CHEMISTRY

LESSONS 29–33

Briefly explain how chemistry is used in the making of each of the following items.

1. Perfume: **Solvent extraction or steam distillation is used to extract the scent molecules from flowers. These are then combined with alcohol to form perfume.**

2. Rubber: **Sulfur is added to rubber/latex and then the mixture is heated to form molecules that are strong and flexible.**

3. Plastic: **Long flexible polymers are formed from petroleum, and then heated and molded into plastic.**

4. Fireworks: **Energy is added to chemical compounds to excite the electrons through explosions. When electrons return to their normal levels, they release light. Chemistry is also used in the combustion reaction of the black powder.**

5. Rocket fuel: **Liquid hydrogen and oxygen are combined at high temperature to produce the combustion reaction that provides the needed thrust for lifting a rocket.**

Mark each statement as either True or False.

6. _T_ Vulcanization makes rubber useful in most temperatures.

7. _F_ Rubber is made from cellulose.

8. _F_ A polymer is a very short molecule.

9. _T_ Today, synthetic rubber is more widely used than natural rubber.

10. _F_ Perfume smells the same in the bottle as on your skin.

11. _T_ Latex is a natural polymer.

12. _T_ Bakelite was the first useful plastic.

13. _T_ Plastic is an important product in American life.

14. _T_ Fireworks are different colors because of different chemical compounds used.

15. _F_ Recipes for fireworks are freely shared.

16. _F_ Kerosene and carbon dioxide are common rocket fuels today.

17. _T_ Newton's Third law of motion is important in rocket design.

18. _T_ Combustion is a chemical reaction that produces large amounts of heat.

CHALLENGE QUESTIONS

Mark each statement as either True or False.

19. _F_ Scents smell the same on every person.

20. _T_ Silk is a natural polymer.

21. _T_ A milk protein can be used as a glue.

22. _F_ Creating polymers is very difficult.

23. _F_ Flames are always the same color.

24. _T_ Sodium chloride burns with a yellow flame.

25. _T_ Hypergolic rocket fuel is not very common.

26. _T_ Solid rocket engines must use up all of their fuel once they are ignited.

27. _T_ Liquid rocket fuel is used in most space rockets.

28. _F_ It is harder to control the rate at which cryogenic fuel burns than the rate at which solid rocket fuel burns.

29. _T_ Borax, glue, and cornstarch can form a polymer.

30. _F_ Lac is a polymer produced by silkworms.

LESSON 34
FUN WITH CHEMISTRY
UNDERSTANDING CHEMICAL REACTIONS

FINAL PROJECT SUPPLY LIST

Milk (not skim)   Paper towels   Food coloring   Water soluble markers   Liquid dish soap
White glue   Disposable baby diaper   Liquid starch   Scissors   Plastic zipper bags
Eyedropper   Copy of "Fun With Chemistry" worksheet

FUN WITH CHEMISTRY WORKSHEET

•   **See the answers for each activity in the student manual, page 135.**

WHAT DID WE LEARN?

- What was your favorite chemical reaction? **Answers will vary.**

- Why did you like that reaction? **Answers will vary.**

TAKING IT FURTHER

- What do you think will happen if you use skim milk in the first activity? **There are very few fat molecules in skim milk, so adding the soap will make little difference. The colors will eventually mix, but at a much slower rate.**

- What colors would you expect to see separate out of orange ink? Brown ink? **Orange is a combination of yellow and red. Brown is a combination of yellow, red, and blue.**

- Why is it important not to inhale the sodium polyacrylate from the diaper? **Evan a small amount of this chemical will absorb a lot of water, so it can irritate your lungs and your eyes by drying them out.**

ATOMS & MOLECULES

LESSONS 1–34

For each pair of elements, write I if they are most likely to form an ionic bond, C for covalent bond, or M for metallic bond.

1. _I_   Na + Cl
2. _C_ H_2 + O
3. _C_   O + O
4. _I_   K + Br
5. _M_   Al + Al
6. _I_   Mg + O
7. _C_   C + O_2
8. _M_   Ag + Ag
9. _M_   Cu + Cu

Note: elements on opposite sides of the periodic table are likely to form ionic bonds; elements that are both metals (from the left side) will form metallic bonds; elements from the right side (non-metals) usually form covalent bonds.

Fill in the blanks with the terms from below.

10. A _catalyst_ can be used to speed up a chemical reaction.

11. The products of an _exothermic_ reaction have a higher temperature than the reactants.

12. The products of an _endothermic_ reaction have a lower temperature than the reactants.

13. An _enzyme_ is a catalyst that increases the rate of digestion.

14. An acid and a base combine to form a _salt_.

15. A substance is a/an _acid_ if it releases H^+ ions when dissolved in water.

16. A substance is a/an _base_ if it releases OH^- ions when dissolved in water.

- Draw and label a model of a helium atom, which has an atomic number of 2 and an atomic mass of 4.

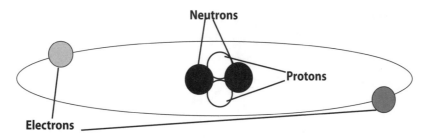

- Choose one of the following topics and briefly explain how chemistry plays a role in it: Farming; Medicine; The nitrogen cycle **Farming: Nitrogen and other chemicals are used up in the growing of crops so chemical fertilizers or other methods must be used to replace them. Also, insecticides, herbicides, and fungicides are all chemicals used to improve crop yield. Medicine: Chemicals are used to change the chemical reactions in the body to improve health. Nitrogen cycle: Nitrogen is used by plants, passed on to animals for their use, and then returned to the soil by decomposers.**

Match the term with its definition.

17. _B_ Natural rubber is made from
18. _D_ Synthetic rubber is made from
19. _E_ A long flexible chain of molecules
20. _A_ Process that makes rubber strong and flexible
21. _F_ A natural polymer found in plants
22. _C_ Process of burning that releases large amounts of heat

Short answer:

23. List three characteristics of a metal. **Silvery, solid, malleable, ductile, conduct electricity.**
24. List three characteristics of a non-metal. **Not shiny, poor conductors, usually gas, brittle if solid.**
25. Explain the chemical reaction involved in your favorite experiment from this book. **Answers will vary.**

CHALLENGE QUESTIONS

26. Use the periodic table of the elements to complete the following chart.

Element	Symbol	Atomic #	Atomic mass	# electrons	# protons	# neutrons
Iron	Fe	**26**	**55.85**	**26**	**26**	**30**
Potassium	**K**	**19**	**39.1**	**19**	**19**	**20**
Mercury	**Hg**	80	**200.5**	**80**	**80**	**120 or 121**
Krypton	**Kr**	**36**	**83.8**	**36**	36	**48**

Fill in the blanks with the words from below.

27. Temperature can increase the _**reaction rate**_ of a chemical reaction.
28. The elements in the first column of the periodic table are _**alkali metals**_.
29. The elements in the last column of the periodic table are _**noble gases**_.
30. The elements in the center of the periodic table are _**transition metals**_.
31. The elements in the second column of the periodic table are _**alkali-earth metals**_.
32. A bioceramic that does not react with the body is a/an _**inert ceramic**_.
33. A bioceramic that dissolves in the body is a/an _**resorbable ceramic**_.
34. An acid is a _**proton donor**_.

35. A base is a **_proton acceptor_**.

36. Molecules that have water bonded to them are **_hydrates_**.

37. A **_homogeneous catalyst_** is in the same phase as the reactants.

38. A **_heterogeneous catalyst_** is in a different phase from the reactants.

LESSON 35
CONCLUSION
APPRECIATING OUR ORDERLY UNIVERSE

SUPPLY LIST

Bible

PROPERTIES OF MATTER

UNIT 1
EXPERIMENTAL SCIENCE

LESSON 1
INTRODUCTION TO EXPERIMENTAL SCIENCE

LEARNING ABOUT MATTER

SUPPLY LIST

Wooden spoon   Metal spoon   Ruler   Pencil   Butter knife   Large cup hot water
Butter or margarine   Stopwatch   Copy of "Conducting Heat Experiment" worksheet

WHAT DID WE LEARN?

- What is matter? **Anything that has mass and takes up space.**
- What do chemists study? **They study the way matter reacts with other matter and the environment.**
- What is an experiment? **A controlled test.**

TAKING IT FURTHER

- Why is it important to study chemistry? **Chemistry is important to every other area of science.**
- What are two things you need to know before conducting an experiment? **The purpose and what you expect to happen.**

LESSON 2
THE SCIENTIFIC METHOD

HOW DO SCIENTISTS DO IT?

SUPPLY LIST

3 empty plastic bottles   Masking tape   Yeast   Marker   Sugar
Cloth tape measure or string   Molasses   3 identical balloons   Thermometer
Measuring cup and spoons   Copy of "Scientific Method" worksheet

SCIENTIFIC METHOD WORKSHEET

- **Taste, color, and texture are all affected by the sweetener used, so even if molasses produces the most gas, you may not like the way it makes your bread taste or look.**

WHAT DID WE LEARN?

- What is the overall job of a scientist? **To systematically study the physical world.**

- What are some areas that cannot be studied by science? **Morality, religion, philosophy, history.**
- What are the five steps of the scientific method? **Learn or observe, ask a question, make a hypothesis, design and perform a test, check the results, and draw conclusions.**

TAKING IT FURTHER

- Why was it necessary to have bottle number 1 in the experiment? **Bottle 1 had only water and yeast. This is called a control. It shows how much gas was produced without a sweetener, so you can tell exactly how much gas was caused by adding the sugar and molasses in the other bottles.**
- What other sweeteners could you try in your experiment? **Honey, corn syrup, fruit juice.**
- What sweeteners were used in the bread at your house? **Look at the ingredients list on the package if you do not bake your own bread. Possible answers are sugar, corn syrup, and honey.**
- Why do you think the company used that sweetener? **Reasons vary, but amount of gas produced, cost, color, and taste are all important factors in why companies use the ingredients they do.**

LESSON 3

TOOLS OF SCIENCE

USING THE RIGHT TOOL FOR THE JOB

SUPPLY LIST

Thermometer   Masking tape   Liquid measuring cup   Marker   Small box   Tennis ball
2 cups   Metric ruler or meter stick   Digital stop watch   Copy of "Scientific Tools" worksheet
Supplies for Challenge (if available): Microscope   Prepared slides   Telescope

SCIENTIFIC TOOLS WORKSHEET

- **Answers to "Summary" questions: Quantitative measurements are more accurate. In general, quantitative measurements are more useful; however, this depends on what you are trying to accomplish. It is not always necessary to make quantitative measurements. You may only need to know if something is warm or melted without having to measure its temperature, for example.**

WHAT DID WE LEARN?

- What is the main thing a scientist does as he/she studies the physical world? **Makes observations.**
- What are the two types of observations that a scientist can make? **Qualitative observations are ones made by the 5 senses without numerical data. Quantitative measurements or observations are made using instruments that generate numerical or other objective data.**
- What is the main problem with qualitative measurements? **The observations may vary from person to person because we each perceive things differently.**
- What are some scientific tools used for quantitative observations? **Balance, graduated cylinder, thermometer, meter stick, spectrometer, etc.**

TAKING IT FURTHER

- What qualitative observations might you make when observing the experiment in lesson 1? **You might observe that the metal spoon is hotter than a wooden spoon or that butter begins to melt faster or slower on certain items.**

- What quantitative observations might you make when observing the experiment in lesson 1? **You might measure the temperature of the water and the temperature of each item. You did measure the length of time it took for the butter to begin to melt on each item. You could also measure the length of time it takes for the butter to completely melt on each item.**

THE METRIC SYSTEM
STANDARD UNITS

SUPPLY LIST

Measuring cup (metric)   Meter stick   Pencil   Paper clip

USING METRIC UNITS

A. **1 liter**   B. **20,000 grams**   C. **4000 meters**   D. **6 centimeters**   E. **500 decigrams**

WHAT DID WE LEARN?

- What are some units used to measure length in the Old English/American measuring system? **Inch, foot, yard, mile, rod, hand, span.**
- What is the unit used to measure length in the metric system? **Meter.**
- What metric unit is used for measuring mass? **Gram.**
- What metric unit is used for measuring liquid volume? **Liter.**
- Why do scientists use the metric system instead of another measuring system? **It is easy to convert from one unit to another, and it is based on only a few basic units. In fact, liters and grams are actually based on the meter. For example, the liter is actually the volume of a cube that is .1 X .1 X .1 meters and a gram is the mass of 1/1000 of a liter, or one cubic centimeter, of water.**

TAKING IT FURTHER

- What metric unit would be best to use to measure the distance across a room? **Meters would be the best unit.**
- What metric unit would you use to measure the distance from one town to another? **The distance would be a very large number if you used meters, so kilometers would be a better choice.**
- What metric unit would you use to measure the width of a hair? **This is much smaller than a meter, so a millimeter or micrometer would be a better choice.**

CHALLENGE: MEASURING SCALES

- **Earthquakes are measured by the Richter scale which measures the intensity of the quake and the Mercalli scale which measures the damage done by the earthquake.**

EXPERIMENTAL SCIENCE

LESSONS 1–4

Number the steps of the scientific method in the correct order.

A. _2_ Ask a question.

B. _1_ Learn about something/Make observations.

C. _6_ Share your results.

D. _4_ Design a test and perform it.

E. _3_ Make a hypothesis.

F. _5_ Check your results/Is your hypothesis right?

Mark each statement as either True or False.

1. _F_ You must always have a correct hypothesis.

2. _T_ It is important to control variables in your experiments.

3. _F_ Qualitative observations always use numbers.

4. _T_ Quantitative observations can be more useful to scientists than qualitative observations.

5. _T_ It is usually easier to make conversions between units in the metric system than in the Old English/ American system.

6. _T_ A millimeter is smaller than a meter.

7. _F_ A graduated cylinder should be used to measure mass.

8. _T_ God has established laws to govern how chemicals react with each other.

9. _F_ Science can always tell us why things happen.

10. _F_ Matter has no mass.

11. Describe what chemistry is the study of. **Chemistry is the study of matter and how it reacts.**

CHALLENGE QUESTIONS

Short answer:

12. Is the measurement of the intensity of light from a distant star origins science or observation science? **Observation.**

13. Is the use of distant starlight to date the universe an example of origins science or observation science? **Origins.**

14. Why shouldn't you look through the eyepiece while lowering the objective on a microscope? **You could run the lens into the slide, causing damage.**

15. How are microscopes similar to telescopes? **They both use lenses to make an image larger.**

16. How are microscopes different from telescopes? **Microscopes only use lenses; telescopes sometimes use mirrors too; microscopes are used to view tiny objects; telescopes are used to view far away objects.**

Match the scale with what phenomenon it describes.

17. _C_ Mohs scale

18. _A_ Fujita scale

19. _E_ Saffir-Simpson scale

20. _B_ Beaufort scale

21. _D_ Richter scale

22. _F_ Mercalli scale

MEASURING MATTER

LESSON 5

MASS VERSUS WEIGHT

WHAT'S THE DIFFERENCE?

SUPPLY LIST

Ruler   Thin rubber band   String   2 pencils   3 paper cups   Paper   25 pennies
Tape   Several paper clips   Single-hole punch
Supplies for Challenge: Copy of "Mass & Weight Units" worksheet

WHAT DID WE LEARN?

- What is the difference between mass and weight? **Mass is the amount of material there is in an object and weight is how much gravity pulls down on an object.**
- How do you measure mass? **By using a balance to compare an object to a known mass.**
- How do you measure weight? **By using a spring scale that is marked for known weights.**

TAKING IT FURTHER

- What would your weight be in outer space? **Nearly zero because there is very little gravity in space.**
- What would your mass be in outer space? **The same as it is on earth.**
- Name a place in the universe where you might go to increase your weight without changing your mass. **Any of the larger planets such as Jupiter or Saturn. Of course, you cannot really go there and you could not survive there if you could, but the gravity is much higher there than on earth so you would weigh much more there.**

CHALLENGE: MASS & WEIGHT UNITS WORKSHEET

1. _Weight_   2. _Mass_   3. _Mass_   4. _Weight_   5. _Weight_   6. _Mass_
7. _Weight_   8. _Mass_   9. _Mass_   10. _Mass_   11. _Mass_   12. _Weight_

LESSON 6

CONSERVATION OF MASS

WHERE DOES IT GO?

SUPPLY LIST

2 paper cups   Balance from lesson 5   2 sugar cubes

Supplies for Challenge: Bottle   Gram scale   Vinegar   Baking soda   Balloon
Copy of "Conservation of Mass" worksheet

What did we learn?

- What is the law of conservation of mass? **Matter cannot be created nor destroyed. It can change form, but it does not go away.**

- How is the mass of water changed when it turns to ice? **It does not change.**

Taking it further

- If you start with 10 grams of water and you boil it until there is no water left in the pan, what happened to the water? **The 10 grams of water turned into 10 grams of steam and entered the air, but it did not disappear or go away.**

- Why is the law of conservation of mass important to understanding the beginning of the world? **It shows that matter cannot create itself or be created by anything in nature. Therefore it had to be created by something outside of nature. We know from the Bible that all matter was created by God.**

Challenge: Conservation of Mass worksheet

- **The mass of the bottle, liquid, and paper is less after the reaction because some of the matter turned into gas and escaped from the bottle. The missing mass is in the CO_2 molecules. Mass should not change when using the balloon, but if it does, it is likely that some gas escaped around the edge of the balloon.**

LESSON
7

Volume

How much space does it take up?

Supply list

Meter stick   Small box   Metric ruler   Small object (eraser, toy, etc.)
Liquid measuring cup
Supplies for Challenge: Box of dry food   Tennis ball   Can of food   Ice cream cone
Die (6-sided)   Copy of "Calculating Volume" worksheet

What did we learn?

- What is volume? **The amount of room or space something occupies.**

- Does air have volume? **Yes, even though you can't see it, it still takes up space. It expands to fill up the available space. Think about a balloon. The air forces the balloon to expand; visibly showing how much room the air is taking up.**

Taking it further

- If you have a cube that is 10 centimeters on each side, what would its volume be? **10 cm x 10 cm x 10 cm = 1000 cubic centimeters.**

- Why is volume important to a scientist? **The volume of matter can be related to many things that scientists are interested in. For example, the volume that a certain amount of fuel occupies determines how a vehicle will be designed.**

CHALLENGE: CALCULATING VOLUME WORKSHEET

- **Answers will vary. Be sure student correctly used each formula.**

LESSON 8

DENSITY

DOES IT FEEL HEAVY?

SUPPLY LIST

Ping-pong ball   Golf ball   Balance from lesson 5   Pennies   Paper clips
Liquid measuring cup
Supplies for Challenge: Metal spoon   Marble   Eraser   Plastic cap   Quarter
Copy of "Density Experiment" worksheet

MEASURING DENSITY

- How did the mass of the golf ball compare to the mass of the ping-pong ball? **It should be significantly more.**
- How did the volume of the golf ball compare to the volume of the ping-pong ball? **It should be about the same.**
- Which ball has a higher density? **The golf ball.**

WHAT DID WE LEARN?

- What is the definition of density? **The mass of an object divided by its volume.**
- If two substances with the same volume have different densities how can you tell which one is the densest? **If they have the same volume, the one that is heavier will have the higher density.**

TAKING IT FURTHER

- If you have two unknown substances that both appear to be silvery colored, how can you tell if they are the same material? **Measure their densities. Platinum has a density of 21.45 g/cc, lead is 11.3 g/cc and aluminum is 2.7 g/cc. This may give you a clue to the material's identity.**
- If two objects have the same density and the same size what will be true about their masses? **They will have the same mass.**
- If you suspect that someone is trying to pass off a gold plated bar of lead as a solid gold bar, how can you test your theory? **Measure the density of the bar. Gold has a density of 19.3 g/cc while lead has a density of 11.3 g/cc. Even though lead may seem heavy, it is not as dense as gold.**
- Why does the ping-pong ball have a lower density than the golf ball? **It is filled with air. Air is very light compared to most substances. The golf ball is filled with plastic, rubber, or other solid materials.**

CHALLENGE: DENSITY EXPERIMENT WORKSHEET

- **Answers will vary. Be sure student used the correct procedure to calculate density.**

BUOYANCY

IT FLOATS!

SUPPLY LIST

Rubbing alcohol   Vegetable oil   Modeling clay   Popcorn (including some unpopped kernels)
2 cups

Supplies for Challenge: Tall narrow glass   Marble   Tape   Marker   Modeling clay
Helium balloon (optional)

TESTING BUOYANCY

- Activity 1: Which shape floats? **If you formed the boat carefully, you should be able to get it to float, whereas the ball will probably sink.**

- Activity 2: What did you observe happening? **You should see the fluffy pieces rise to the top and the unpopped kernels sink to the bottom. The kernels are denser than the popped pieces. The popped pieces take up more space, but have the same amount of matter as the kernels so they are less dense and thus rise to the top.**

- Activity 3: What happened to the oil in each cup? **You should have observed that the oil floated on the top of the water but sank to the bottom of the alcohol.**

- Why did the oil float in one cup but sink in the other? **Oil is less dense than water but more dense than alcohol. The oil is buoyant in the water but not in the alcohol.**

WHAT DID WE LEARN?

- What is buoyancy? **The ability to float.**

- If something is buoyant, what does that tell you about its density compared to that of the substance in which it floats? **It means that the object's density is less than the density of the substance that it is floating on.**

- Are you buoyant in water? **Probably, especially if you are holding your breath.**

TAKING IT FURTHER

- What are some substances that are buoyant in water besides you? **Ivory soap, a leaf, paper, oil, etc.**

- Based on what you observed, which is denser, water or alcohol? **Water is denser. Oil will float on the water but sinks in the alcohol.**

- Why is a foam swimming tube or a foam life ring able to keep a person afloat in the water? **Foam is a material that has air trapped in it so it is not very dense. Even with the person's weight/mass added to it, the foam object's density remains lower than the density of the water.**

- Why is it important to life that ice is less dense than water? **Otherwise rivers and lakes would freeze from the bottom up, and no life could survive in them.**

QUIZ 2

MEASURING MATTER

LESSONS 5–9

Match the term with its definition.

1. _C_ The amount of a substance

2. _H_ How strongly something is pulled on by gravity

3. _A_ Matter cannot be created or destroyed

4. _D_ How much space matter occupies

5. _B_ How much mass is in a particular volume

6. _G_ The ability for one substance to float in another

7. _F_ Used to measure mass

8. _E_ Used to measure weight

9. _J_ A material that is denser than lead

10. _I_ Only material to become less dense when frozen

Short answer:

11. Explain how the water you drink today could be the same water a dinosaur drank thousands of years ago. **Water is recycled. After a dinosaur drank water it exhaled some water into the atmosphere. That water has been recycled through the water cycle for thousands of years.**

12. Explain what happens to nitrogen in the soil and in plants that demonstrates conservation of mass. **Nitrogen is absorbed by plants, eaten by animals, then returned to the soil when the plant or animal dies. It does not get used up.**

13. If an object floats in one liquid but sinks in another, what does that tell you about the densities of the two liquids? **The first liquid is denser than the second.**

14. How would you determine the volume of a toy car? **Use the displacement method.**

15. How are buoyancy and density related? **One substance is buoyant in another if it is less dense than the other substance.**

CHALLENGE QUESTIONS

Short answer:

16. What are two units for measuring mass? **Grams, slugs.**

17. What are two units for measuring weight? **Newtons, pounds.**

18. If you perform an experiment and the mass of the resulting substance is less than the mass of what you started with, what is one likely explanation? **It is likely that a gas was produced and escaped from the experiment. A nuclear reaction converts a small amount of mass into energy.**

19. Which is likely to be more dense, a one inch cube of steel or a one inch cube of wood? **Steel is denser than wood.**

20. If you are traveling in a car with a helium balloon and the driver suddenly puts on the brakes, what will happen to your body and what will happen to the balloon? **Your momentum will carry your body forward as the car suddenly slows down. It will also carry air molecules forward. Helium is lighter than the air so the balloon will move backward to take the place of the air molecules.**

LESSON 10
PHYSICAL & CHEMICAL PROPERTIES

IS IT SOMETHING NEW?

SUPPLY LIST

Sauce pan   Ice   Salt   Lemon juice   Baking soda   Cup

Supplies for Challenge: Copy of "Physical or Chemical Properties" worksheet

PHYSICAL & CHEMICAL CHANGES

1. **Ice melting is a physical change; no other elements were added to the water and it just changed state without becoming something else. Salt dissolving in water is also a physical change.**

2. **The salt molecules are moved farther away from each other, but they are not combined with the water to form something new.**

3. **The fact that the salt remains behind is a good clue that it did not react with the water.**

4. **The lemon juice and baking soda is a chemical change. The fact that bubbles are generated is a clue that some kind of gas is being generated, indicating a new substance being formed.**

WHAT DID WE LEARN?

- What are some physical properties of matter? **These could include color, texture, temperature, density, mass, state, etc.**

- What is a chemical change? **When two or more substances combine to form a different substance.**

- Give an example of a chemical change. **There are innumerable examples. Some common chemical changes that might be mentioned include photosynthesis, hydrogen and oxygen combining to form water, vinegar and baking soda combining to form carbon dioxide, yeast turning sugar into carbon dioxide, rust, digesting food, etc.**

TAKING IT FURTHER

- How can you determine if a change in matter is a physical change or a chemical change? **Find out if the ending matter is the same type of matter as what you started with. Chemical changes often involve release of energy such as heat, light, or sound.**

- Diamond and quartz appear to have very similar physical properties. They are both clear crystalline substances. However, diamond is much harder than quartz. How would this affect their effectiveness as tips for drill bits? **The quartz-tipped drill would quickly wear down and be ineffective. Diamond-tipped drills are very hard and very effective at drilling through nearly any other substance. It is important to understand physical properties of matter as well as chemical properties.**

MATTER

CHALLENGE: PHYSICAL OR CHEMICAL PROPERTIES WORKSHEET

1. _P_ Liquid water becoming steam
2. _C_ Flavor/taste   **Primarily C (P—texture contributes to taste)**
3. _C_ Burning of wood/fire
4. _P_ Filling a balloon with air
5. _P_ Softness
6. _P_ Making ice cream **(The sugar & milk mixture is frozen but does not become something else.)**
7. _C_ Digesting food **(Some physical aspects but is primarily chemical.)**
8. _P_ Straightening a paper clip
9. _P_ Cloud formation
10. _C_ Rust on a piece of iron
11. _C_ Separation of water into hydrogen and oxygen gases
12. _P_ Dissolving sugar in water
13. _C_ Photosynthesis
14. _C_ Bacteria decaying dead plant matter
15. _P_ Shine/luster
16. _C_ A cake rising in the oven **(Gas is produced.)**
17. _P_ Cutting a piece of wood
18. _C_ Bread rising
19. _P_ Hardness
20. _P or C_ Making perfume **(Depends on the process.)**

MATTER

LESSON
11 STATES OF MATTER

PHASE CHANGES

SUPPLY LIST

Ice   Small saucepan   Hand mirror   Ice tray   Access to stove and freezer

Supplies for Challenge: Jar   Marker   Water

OBSERVING PHASE CHANGES

*   How does it feel? **Hard, cold, smooth.**
*   How does the liquid compare to the solid? **It is warmer, can be moved easier, wet.**
*   What did you notice as the water began to boil? **Little bubbles came up from the bottom of the pan. Steam rose from the water.**
*   How does the water on the mirror feel? **Cool and wet.**
*   How does the water look and feel now? **Cold, hard, smooth.**

What did we learn?

- What are the three physical states of most matter? **Solid, liquid, gas.**

- What is the name for each phase change? **Solid to liquid is melting, liquid to gas is evaporation, gas to liquid is condensation, liquid to solid is freezing, and for those substances that can go directly from solid to gas or gas to solid, the phase change is called sublimation.**

- What is required to bring about a phase change in a substance? **The addition or removal of energy—primarily in the form of heat.**

Taking it further

- Name several substances that are solid at room temperature. **The answers are endless. Some ideas include metals, wood, plastic, many foods, people, animals, etc.**

- Name several substances that are liquid at room temperature. **Some ideas include water, juice, tea, honey, rubbing alcohol, and syrup.**

- Name several substances that are gas at room temperature. **Some ideas include air, nitrogen, oxygen, hydrogen, carbon dioxide, carbon monoxide, propane, and natural gas.**

LESSON 12

SOLIDS

HARD AS A ROCK

Supply list

Wooden block   Honey   Rock   Metal spoon

Testing For Solids

1. Does it take up the same amount of room if you put it in another container? **All four objects will take up the same amount of space. This is a characteristic of solids and liquids because they do not expand to fill their containers.**

2. Is it denser than air, or does it float in air? **None of these objects floats, so they are all denser than air. Being dense is a characteristic of most solids and liquids.**

3. Does its shape stay the same if I move it or put it in another container? **The honey will not keep its shape, but the others will; therefore, honey cannot be a solid.**

4. Is it a solid? **If you answered yes to all three questions, the object is a solid. Honey is not a solid because it does not keep its shape, but wood, rocks and spoons are solid.**

What did we learn?

- What are three characteristics of solids? **They keep their shape, they have a definite volume, they are denser than most liquids and gases, and their molecules are closely packed together.**

- How do large crystals form in solids? **If the liquid cools down very slowly, the molecules may be able to line up in regular patterns to make crystals.**

- What state is the most common for the basic elements? **Nearly 90% of the elements are solids.**

TAKING IT FURTHER

- Is Silly Putty a solid or a liquid? **Silly Putty may seem like a solid, yet if you leave it sitting in one place for very long, it will start to flatten out. Because it does not hold its shape it is really a very thick liquid.**

LESSON 13

LIQUIDS

CAN YOU POUR IT?

SUPPLY LIST

Water   Hand lotion   Vegetable Oil   Dish soap   Honey   Baking sheet
Copy of "Viscosity" worksheet
Supplies for Challenge: Cup of water

WHAT DID WE LEARN?

- Which has more kinetic energy, a solid or a liquid? **A liquid.**
- What shape does a liquid have? **The shape of its container.**
- What is viscosity? **A measure of how strongly the liquid's molecules are attracted to each other.**

TAKING IT FURTHER

- How is a liquid similar to a solid? **Both a solid and a liquid are much denser than a gas, both have a definite volume that can be measured, the molecules of both are close together.**
- How is a liquid different from a solid? **Its molecules move freely over one another and its shape changes when you put it in a different container.**
- How would you change a solid into a liquid? **You melt it by adding more energy, usually in the form of heat.**

LESSON 14

GASES

LIGHTER THAN AIR?

SUPPLY LIST

2 tennis balls (Note: place 1 of the balls in the freezer about 30 minutes before you plan to use it.)
Supplies For Challenge: Perfume   Cup   Step ladder

OBSERVING AIR PRESSURE

- Why does a ball bounce? **It is because the air molecules inside the ball are pressing against the inside of the ball. So when a ball hits the floor, the molecules inside it push back against the floor, causing the ball to bounce up.**
- Do gas molecules move faster when they are warm or when they are cold? **The warmer the molecules are, the faster they will be moving.**

- Which ball bounced highest? **The warm ball will bounce higher.**
- Why does the warmer ball bounce higher? **The molecules inside the ball are moving faster so more particles collide with the inside of the ball when it hits the floor. This gives the warm ball more energy to bounce back than the cold ball has.**

What did we learn?

- When is a substance called a gas? **When it has enough energy for the molecules to break apart from each other and move freely.**
- What is the shape of a gas? **It takes on the shape of its container.**
- In which state of matter are the molecules moving the fastest? **In a gas.**
- What is atmospheric pressure? **The pressure applied to a surface by the collision of the air molecules with that surface.**

Taking it further

- How is a gas similar to a liquid? **The molecules of both a gas and a liquid can move around and they both take on the shape of their containers.**
- How is a gas different from a liquid? **Gas molecules have much more energy, they freely move away from each other, and they collide with other molecules and objects billions of times a second. Gas expands to fill its container so it does not have a definite volume.**
- Why is it necessary that a space suit be pressurized in outer space? **God designed our bodies to operate in an environment where there is pressure on our bodies. If this pressure were not there, we would die. Since there is no air in space there is no air pressure, so space suits must provide the pressure necessary for the astronauts.**

LESSON

15 Gas Laws

Rules to live by

Supply list

Empty 1-gallon milk carton   Balloon   Microwave oven
Cloth tape measure or string and a ruler   Access to a freezer
Supplies for Challenge: Plastic ½-liter or 1-liter bottle   Dish soap   Hot and cold water

What did we learn?

- If temperature remains constant, what happens to the volume of a gas when the pressure is increased? **The volume decreases.**
- If pressure remains constant, what happens to the volume of a gas when the temperature is increased? **The volume increases.**
- What are two different ways to increase the volume of a gas? **Decrease the pressure or increase the temperature.**

Taking it further

- Why might you need to check the air in your bike tires before you go for a ride on a cold day? **The volume of air may be decreased enough by the cold temperatures that you may need to add some air so your tires will not be flat.**

- Why do you think increasing pressure decreases the volume of a gas? **The pressure forces the molecules closer together so they take up less space.**

- Why do you think increasing temperature increases the volume of a gas? **The increase in the temperature adds energy to the molecules causing them to move faster so they spread out more and take up more space.**

- What might happen to the volume of a gas when the pressure is increased and the temperature is increased at the same time? **It depends on how much the pressure and temperature are increased. It is possible that the volume could remain the same. It could also increase or decrease. Because you are changing two things at once, you can't be certain of the effect without knowing how much you are changing each condition.**

QUIZ 3 STATES OF MATTER

LESSONS 10–15

Use the terms from the list below to fill in the blanks.

1. The three states of matter are _**solid**_, _**liquid**_, and _**gas**_.
2. _**Adding heat**_ causes the molecules in matter to move more quickly.
3. _**Removing heat**_ causes the molecules in matter to move more slowly.
4. _**Removing heat**_ is required to change a gas into a liquid.
5. _**Adding heat**_ is required to change a solid into a liquid.

Write S beside the statement if it describes a property of a solid, L if it describes a liquid, and G if it describes a gas. Some statements describe more than one state of matter.

6. _**S, L**_ Molecules are close together.
7. _**G**_ Molecules are far apart.
8. _**L, G**_ It takes on the shape of its container.
9. _**G**_ Molecules move very quickly.
10. _**L**_ Molecules slide over each other.
11. _**G**_ Easily compressed.
12. _**S**_ Has a defined shape.
13. _**S, L**_ Has a defined volume.
14. _**S**_ Molecules only vibrate.
15. _**S, L**_ Not easily compressed.

Mark each statement as either True or False.

16. _**T**_ Thick liquids have a high viscosity.
17. _**F**_ As the temperature of a gas increases, its volume decreases.
18. _**T**_ As the pressure of a gas increases, its volume decreases.

19. _T_ A ball will usually bounce better on a warm day than on a cold one.

20. _F_ Molecules in a viscous liquid are not strongly attracted to each other.

21. _T_ There is a direct relationship between the temperature of a gas and its volume.

22. _T_ Crystals are more likely to form when a solid cools slowly.

CHALLENGE QUESTIONS

Mark each statement as either True or False.

23. _T_ Solid water is less dense than liquid water.

24. _T_ Glass can be classified as an amorphous solid.

25. _F_ Evaporation requires that a liquid be heated to the boiling point.

26. _F_ Diffusion occurs as molecules move from an area of lower concentration to an area of higher concentration.

27. _T_ Glass does not have a definite boiling point.

28. _F_ All solids are denser than their liquid form.

29. _F_ Evaporation is slower on windy days.

30. _T_ Increasing surface area increases evaporation rate.

Identify each of the following changes as a chemical change or a physical change.

31. _Physical_ Adding water to orange juice.

32. _Physical_ Shredding a piece of paper.

33. _Chemical_ Taking aspirin for a headache

34. _Chemical_ Burning a candle

35. _Chemical_ Shooting off fireworks

CLASSIFYING MATTER

LESSON 16

ELEMENTS

THE BASIC BUILDING BLOCKS

SUPPLY LIST

Jigsaw puzzle

Supplies for Challenge: Copy of "Learning about the Elements" worksheet

WHAT DID WE LEARN?

- What is an element? **It is a substance that cannot be broken down by ordinary chemical means—an atom.**

- What is a compound? **It is a substance that is formed when two or more elements combine chemically—a molecule.**

- What is a mixture? **It is a combination of two or more substances that do not make a new substance.**

TAKING IT FURTHER

- If a new element was discovered and it was named newmaterialium, would you expect it to be a metal or a non-metal? **It would probably be a metal because most metal names end in "um" or "ium."**

- Is salt an element, a compound or a mixture? **Salt is a compound made from sodium and chlorine. It can be broken apart into its elements. But when they are put together they form a new substance.**

- Is soda pop an element, compound or mixture? **It is a mixture of water, sugar, flavorings, and other substances, but it is not a new substance.**

CHALLENGE: LEARNING ABOUT THE ELEMENTS WORKSHEET

Name	Symbol	Atomic number
Hydrogen	**H**	1
Oxygen	**O**	8
Aluminum	**Al**	13
Silicon	**Si**	14
Mercury	**Hg**	80

Metal	Metalloid	Non-metal
Sodium	**Germanium**	**Nitrogen**
Gold	**Polonium**	**Phosphorus**
Barium	**Arsenic**	**Fluorine**
Potassium	**Antimony**	**Neon**
Calcium	**Boron**	**Chlorine**
Silver		

Magnesium—12

Argon—18

Sulfur—16

Iron—26

Copper—29

Bismuth—83

Platinum—78

Radon—86

LESSON 17

COMPOUNDS

MAKING NEW SUBSTANCES

SUPPLY LIST

2 small jars (small baby food jars or test tubes)   Copper wire (at least 3 feet)   Baking soda
6-volt battery (big square battery)

ELECTROLYSIS OF WATER

1. What do you think is in each jar? **Students may suggest air. The correct answer is hydrogen in one jar and oxygen in the other.**

2. Which jar do you think has the hydrogen in it? **The jar that has more gas has the hydrogen. Remember, there are 2 hydrogen atoms for every oxygen atom in the water.**

3. Why do you think the battery is needed to separate the atoms? **Energy is required to break the bonds of the molecule, and the battery supplies electrical energy.**

WHAT DID WE LEARN?

*   What is a compound? **A substance that is formed when two or more different kinds of atoms are chemically joined together.**

*   What is another name for an element? **An atom.**

*   What is another name for compound? **A molecule.**

*   Do compounds behave the same way as the atoms that they are made from? **Not usually. Oxygen gas and hydrogen gas act very differently than liquid water or water vapor.**

TAKING IT FURTHER

*   The symbol for carbon dioxide is CO_2. What atoms combine to form this molecule? **One carbon atom and two oxygen atoms.**

*   The air consists of nitrogen and oxygen molecules. Is air a compound? Why or why not? **The air is not a compound because the nitrogen and oxygen molecules do not bond with each other to form a different substance. Instead, air is a mixture of gases.**

LESSON 18

WATER

GOD'S COMPOUND FOR LIFE

SUPPLY LIST

Copy of "Water, Water Everywhere" worksheet
Supplies for Challenge: Three 2-liter plastic bottles   Cotton string   Potting soil   Bean seeds
Ice water

Water, Water Everywhere worksheet

- **Food, water, beverages, washing dishes, cooking, making ice, growing house plants, water for pets, brushing teeth, toilets, bath/shower, washing hands/face, wiping counters, washing windows, laundry, mopping floors, watering grass, breathing, sweating/cooling your body, digestion, blood circulation, blinking, elimination of wastes, making of new cells, etc.**

What did we learn?

- What two kinds of atoms combine to form water? **Hydrogen and oxygen.**

- Why is water called a universal solvent? **Because a large variety of substances can be dissolved in water.**

- What is unique about the water molecule that makes it able to dissolve so many substances? **The hydrogen atoms attach to the oxygen atom at a 105° angle, causing the charge to be unevenly distributed.**

Taking it further

- What would happen to your body if oxygen could not be dissolved in water? **Your blood would not be able to take oxygen to the cells in your body and you would die.**

- Is water truly a universal solvent? **No, there are many substances, particularly oils and fats, that do not dissolve in water.**

- Why is it important for mothers with nursing babies to drink lots of water? **Water is used in the production of milk.**

LESSON 19

Mixtures

All mixed up

Supply list

Coffee filter   Orange juice   Funnel   Cup

What did we learn?

- What are two differences between a compound and a mixture? **A compound is formed when two or more elements combine to form a new substance. A mixture is formed when two or more elements or compounds are combined but do not form a new substance. The elements in a compound are always in the same proportion. The elements or compounds in a mixture can be in any proportion.**

- What is a homogeneous mixture? **One in which all of the substances are evenly distributed.**

- What is a heterogeneous mixture? **One in which all of the substances are not evenly distributed.**

- Name three common mixtures. **Air, milk, granite, orange juice, and seawater.**

Taking it further

- If a soft metal is combined with a gas to form a hard solid that doesn't look or act like either of the original substances, is the resulting substance a mixture or a compound? **The result is a compound because the new substance has different characteristics from the original substances. In a mixture, the substances retain their original properties.**

- How might you separate the salt from the sand and water in a sample of seawater? **First, you could filter out the sand. Then you could let the water evaporate into the air and the salt would be left behind. This is similar to the experiment you did in lesson 6 with sugar and water.**

CHALLENGE: SEPARATING COMPOUNDS

Cream and milk: **Centrifuge**   Mud and water: **Decantation or filtering**   Food colors: **Chromatography**
Lemon juice and water: **Evaporation**   Oil and water: **Decantation**   Coffee and coffee grounds: **Filtering or decantation.**

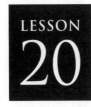

LESSON 20

AIR
WHAT WE BREATHE

SUPPLY LIST

Candle   Jar   Bottle   Baking soda   Vinegar

WHAT DID WE LEARN?

- What is likely the most important element on earth? **Oxygen.**
- What is likely the most important compound on earth? **Water.**
- What is likely the most important mixture on earth? **Air.**
- What are the main components of air? **Oxygen and nitrogen.**

TAKING IT FURTHER

- Why is nitrogen necessary in the air? **Nitrogen dilutes the oxygen.**
- Why is oxygen necessary in air? **Oxygen is necessary for cellular respiration in all plants and animals.**
- How does the composition of air show God's provision for life? **Air provides exactly what is necessary for life without harming life on earth.**

LESSON 21

MILK & CREAM
UDDERLY DELICIOUS

SUPPLY LIST

2 cups liquid whipping cream   Jar with lid   Sugar   Vanilla extract   Bowl   Plate
Canned spray whipping cream (made with real cream)   Electric mixer
Supplies for Challenge: Whole milk   Vinegar   Pan   Access to stove

WHAT DID WE LEARN?

- Is milk an element, a compound, or a mixture? **Milk is a mixture.**

- What is pasteurization and why is it used on milk? **Pasteurization is the process of heating the milk to kill the bacteria in it.**
- What is homogenization and why is it done to milk? **Homogenization is the process that breaks the fat molecules into tiny bits so they stay suspended in the milk. This prevents the cream from separating from the milk and floating to the top.**
- What is a foam? **It is a liquid that has air molecules suspended in it.**

TAKING IT FURTHER

- Why does whipped cream begin to "weep"? **The fat molecules lose their ability to keep the lighter air molecules trapped and the air eventually escapes.**
- Why must cream be churned in order to make butter? **To form butter, the fat molecules must be forced together. Churning forces the molecules to clump together.**

CLASSIFYING MATTER

LESSONS 16–21

Match the terms below with their correct definition or description.

1. _C_ A combination of two or more pure substances where each keeps its own properties—a new substance is *not* formed.
2. _J_ A liquid with air bubbles trapped in it.
3. _B_ A substance made when two or more elements combine chemically.
4. _G_ The process of heating a mixture to kill the bacteria in it.
5. _A_ A substance that cannot be broken down chemically.
6. _D_ A mixture where the substances are thoroughly mixed up.
7. _E_ A mixture where the substances are not evenly mixed up.
8. _H_ A nearly universal solvent.
9. _I_ The process of breaking up fat into tiny pieces that can remain suspended.
10. _F_ The ability of fat molecules to keep air molecules suspended.

Short answer:

11. Explain why whipped cream eventually melts into a pool of white liquid? **The fat molecules become unable to hold the gas and it escapes.**
12. Give an example showing that a compound does not act like the elements that it is made from. **Accept any reasonable answer such as liquid water does not act like oxygen gas or hydrogen gas.**
13. Explain why water is considered by many to be a nearly universal solvent. **Most substances will dissolve in water because of its unique shape.**
14. What elements are found in the compound CH_4 **Carbon and hydrogen (1 carbon and 4 hydrogen atoms).**

CHALLENGE QUESTIONS

15. What is a mineral? **Compound found in earth's crust.**
16. Name three groups of minerals. **Silicates, carbonates, halides, sulfides, phosphates, oxides.**

MATTER

17. What is a native mineral? **Mineral containing only one element.**

18. List three ways to separate substances in a mixture. **Filtering, decantation, distillation, evaporation, chromatography, centrifuge.**

19. Briefly explain how milk is turned into cheese. **Acid is added to coagulate the milk, curds are separated from the whey, an enzyme is added to harden the curds, curds can be pressed and aged.**

20. What instrument is used to separate blood cells from plasma? **Centrifuge.**

SOLUTIONS

SOLUTIONS

WILL IT DISSOLVE?

SUPPLY LIST

Roll of Life Savers candy   Rolling pin   3 cups   Plastic zipper bag
Copy of "Solutions Experiments" worksheet

Supplies for Challenge: Table salt (sodium chloride)   Potassium salt (Potassium chloride)
Sugar   Baking soda   4 clear cups   Copy of "Solubility of Various Substances" worksheet

SOLUTIONS EXPERIMENTS WORKSHEET

• **Candy will dissolve fastest in hot water. Crushed candy will dissolve faster than whole candy. Candy will dissolve faster if you move your tongue.**

WHAT DID WE LEARN?

• What is a solution? **A mixture in which one substance is dissolved in another.**

• Is a solution a homogeneous or heterogeneous mixture? **A solution is homogeneous.**

• In a solution, what is the name for the substance being dissolved? **The solute.**

• In a solution, what is the substance called in which the solute is dissolved? **The solvent.**

• What is solubility? **The amount of a substance that can be dissolved in a given amount of solvent.**

TAKING IT FURTHER

• Why can more salt be dissolved in hot water than in cold water? **The warmer molecules are moving faster and can hold more salt molecules away from each other so they can dissolve more salt than the slower, colder water molecules.**

• If you want sweet iced tea, would it be better to add the sugar before or after you cool the tea? **If you add the sugar while the tea is hot you will be able to dissolve more sugar and thus the tea will be sweeter. Whether this is better depends on how sweet you like your tea.**

LESSON 23

SUSPENSIONS

AND WE DON'T MEAN GETTING KICKED OUT OF SCHOOL.

SUPPLY LIST

1 egg   Vinegar   Salt   Vegetable oil   Dry mustard   Lemon juice   Paprika
Small mixing bowl   Electric mixer
Supplies for Challenge: Cake mix   Eggs   Oil   Ingredients called for in cake mix

WHAT DID WE LEARN?

- What is a suspension? **A suspension is a mixture of substances that don't dissolve. It has particles of one substance that can stay suspended in the other for a short period of time, but not indefinitely.**

- What does immiscible mean? **Two liquids that do not mix are immiscible.**

- What is an emulsifier? **A substance that keeps immiscible liquids suspended.**

- What is a colloid? **A liquid with very tiny particles suspended in it.**

TAKING IT FURTHER

- What would happen to the mayonnaise if the egg yolk was left out of the recipe? **The oil would separate out and it would lose its creamy texture.**

- How is a suspension different from a true solution? **The molecules that are dissolved in a solution will stay dissolved indefinitely, whereas the particles that are suspended will eventually settle out of a suspension if an emulsifier is not added.**

LESSON 24

SOLUBILITY

HOW WELL DOES IT DISSOLVE?

SUPPLY LIST

2 cans of soda pop (1 at room temperature and 1 chilled)   2 clear cups
Supplies for Challenge: Table salt   Potassium salt   Baking soda   Sugar   Vegetable oil
Dish soap   4 clear cups   Copy of "Like Dissolves Like" worksheet

WARM OR COLD SOLUTIONS

1. What are the main ingredients in the solution you are observing? **Carbon dioxide gas dissolved in water. The solution also contains sugar, but we are interested in observing the gas.**

2. Which cup appears to be more bubbly? **Answers will vary.**

3. Does gas escape more easily from a warm solution or a cold solution? **Warm.**

4. Which cup contains the colder liquid? **The one with fewer escaping bubbles.**

What did we learn?

- What is solubility? **The ability of a solvent to dissolve a solute.**

- What does "like dissolves like" mean? **Solvents dissolve materials that have similar molecular shapes or structures to them.**

- What are the three factors that most affect solubility? **The type of materials being dissolved, temperature and pressure.**

- What is the name given to particles that come out of a saturated solution? **A precipitate or precipitation.**

Taking it further

- Why is soda pop canned or bottled at low temperatures and high pressure? **Soda pop is a solution of carbon dioxide dissolved in a liquid. To keep the maximum amount of gas dissolved, the soda is canned or bottled at low temperatures under high pressure.**

- Why does a bottle of soda pop eventually go flat once it is opened? **The pressure has been reduced on the solution so the liquid cannot hold as much gas as it once did. The gas escapes into the air and the pop tastes flat.**

- If no additional sugar has been added to a saturated solution of sugar water, what can you conclude about the temperature and/or pressure if you notice sugar beginning to settle on the bottom of the cup? **You can conclude that either the temperature of the solution has dropped or the pressure has increased and the water is no longer able to hold all of the sugar in solution.**

Like Dissolves Like worksheet

- **Soap is the only one of these substances that will dissolve in the oil because it is the only one that has a similar molecular structure to oil.**

LESSON
25 Soda Pop

America's (second) favorite drink

Supply list

Club soda   Orange juice   Sugar or corn syrup   Measuring spoons   Vanilla extract
Nutmeg   Cinnamon   Lemon juice   Food coloring (yellow, red, blue)   Baking soda
Supplies for Challenge: Can of regular soda pop   Can of diet soda pop

What did we learn?

- What are the main ingredients of soda pop? **Water, sweetener, flavoring, color, and carbon dioxide.**

- What is the most popular drink in the world? The second most popular? **Water, followed in second place by soda pop.**

- What are the two most popular sweeteners used in soda pop? **Corn syrup and aspartame.**

Taking it further

- Why are soda pop cans warmed and dried before they are boxed? **The soda is very cold when it is canned or bottled. As it warms up, water condenses on the outside of the can or bottle. If this occurred after packaging, the water would make the boxes or cartons soggy, so it is done beforehand.**

- Why are recipes for soda pop considered top secret? **People buy a particular brand of pop because they like that flavor better than any other. So if someone obtained a secret recipe, the original company could lose money.**

- Why would the finished syrup be tested before adding the carbonation? **To ensure that it tastes correctly before it completes the process; to make sure that nothing went wrong in the previous steps.**

LESSON 26 CONCENTRATION

IS YOUR LEMONADE WEAK?

SUPPLY LIST

Milk   Ice   Sugar   Salt   Vanilla extract   Quart-sized plastic zipper bag
Sandwich-sized plastic zipper bag
Supplies for Challenge: Thermometer   Stopwatch   Sauce pan   Baking soda   2 cups
Saltwater   Copy of "Salt's Effect on the Freezing and Boiling Point of Water" worksheet
Access to stove

WHAT DID WE LEARN?

- What is a dilute solution? **One in which there are relatively few solute molecules in the solution.**

- What is a concentrated solution? **One in which there are a relatively large number of solute molecules in the solution.**

- How does the concentration of a solution affect its boiling point? **In general, the more concentrated it is, the higher the boiling point will be.**

- How does the concentration of a solution affect its freezing point? **In general, the more concentrated it is, the lower the freezing point will be.**

TAKING IT FURTHER

- Why is a quantitative observation for concentration usually more useful than a qualitative observation? **Qualitative observations are based on people's perceptions and not easily repeated. One person may think that the lemonade is too strong while another thinks it is too weak. But quantitative observations are not a matter of opinion and can be repeated.**

- If a little antifreeze helps an engine run better, would it be better to add straight antifreeze to the radiator? **Not necessarily. The combination of different molecules raises the boiling point and lowers the freezing point of both substances in the solution, but straight antifreeze would not necessarily have the same effect.**

CHALLENGE: SALT'S EFFECT ON THE FREEZING AND BOILING POINT OF WATER worksheet

- **You should find that salt increases the boiling point and decreases the freezing point of water.**

LESSON 27

SEAWATER

THE WORLD'S MOST COMMON SOLUTION

SUPPLY LIST

Water   Soda straw   Salt   Egg

WHAT DID WE LEARN?

- What is the most common solution on earth? **Seawater.**
- What are the main elements found in the ocean besides water? **Sodium chloride—salt, magnesium, and bromine.**
- How does salt get into the ocean? **Water flowing over land dissolves salt and other minerals and carries them to the ocean. The minerals stay behind when the water evaporates.**
- Name one gas that is dissolved in the ocean water. **Oxygen is the main gas. Nitrogen, carbon dioxide, and other gases are present as well.**

TAKING IT FURTHER

- Why is seawater saltier than water in the rivers and lakes? **Fresh water is continually entering and exiting the rivers and lakes. So the amount of salt remains low. However, in the ocean, the only way that water leaves is through evaporation, which removes the water but leaves the minerals. After thousands of years, the salt has built up in the oceans.**
- Why is there more oxygen near the surface of the ocean than in deeper parts? **Algae and other plants grow near the surface and produce oxygen that dissolves in the water.**

LESSON 28

WATER TREATMENT

MAKING IT CLEAN

SUPPLY LIST

Empty 2-liter plastic bottle   Dirt   Sand   Gravel or small pebbles   Alum   2 cups
Dish or tray   Charcoal briquettes   Plastic zipper bag   Cotton balls   Hammer
Goggles

WHAT DID WE LEARN?

- Why do we need water treatment plants? **Water from rivers and lakes contains dirt, harmful bacteria, and other substances that are not healthy for people to drink.**
- What are the three main things that are done to water to make it clean enough for human consumption? **Particles are allowed to settle out, chemicals are added to kill bacteria, and the water is filtered.**
- Why is it important not to dump harmful chemicals into rivers and lakes? **The chemicals will dissolve in the water and harm the plants and animals living there.**

TAKING IT FURTHER

- How is the filter you built similar to God's design for cleaning the water? **Much of the water that falls on the earth sinks into the ground where it flows through sand and gravel and becomes cleaner before reaching rivers and underground water tables.**

QUIZ 5 SOLUTIONS

LESSONS 22–28

Mark each statement as either True or False.

1. _T_ All solutions are mixtures.

2. _F_ All mixtures are solutions.

3. _F_ A saturated solution can dissolve more solute.

4. _T_ True solutions do not settle out.

5. _F_ Milk is a true solution.

6. _T_ Temperature affects how fast substances dissolve.

7. _T_ Surface area affects how fast substances dissolve.

8. _F_ A dilute solution has a high amount of solute.

9. _T_ The boiling point of a solution is affected by concentration.

10. _T_ Cold liquids can suspend more gas than warmer liquids.

Short answer:

11. Describe why increased pressure decreases the solubility of a solid in a liquid. **Pressure pushes the molecules closer together so the solute molecules will more easily combine and settle out of the solution.**

12. Describe why increased pressure increases the solubility of a gas in a liquid. **Pressure pushes the molecules closer together so the gas molecules cannot escape as easily.**

13. What is a precipitate? **It is a dissolved substance that comes out of the saturated solution.**

14. Why is salt added to ice when freezing ice cream? **Salt lowers the freezing point of the ice, allowing it to absorb more heat from the ice cream mixture and thus making the cream freeze more quickly.**

15. What is likely to happen to a car without antifreeze in the radiator? **The water will boil more easily and could boil over if the temperatures get high. Also, water will freeze more easily and could freeze in the winter time.**

CHALLENGE QUESTIONS

Short answer:

16. If a substance easily dissolves in water would you expect it to easily dissolve in oil? **It is not likely since like dissolves like and water and oil are very different.**

17. Why does soap easily dissolve in both water and oil? **Soap is a unique molecule that is shaped similarly to water on one end and similarly to oil on the other end.**

18. Name one commercial application for an emulsion. **Foods such as mayonnaise, lotions, paints, espresso, photographic film.**

19. How does the concentration of salt affect the boiling point of water? **As salt concentration goes up so does the boiling point.**

20. Why does salt affect the boiling point this way? **The salt molecules prevent the water molecules from reaching the surface and escaping into the air so more energy is needed to bring the solution to a boil.**

21. How does temperature affect the density of sea water? **The colder the water, the closer together the molecules are so the denser it will be.**

22. Why is hard water considered a problem? **Hard water can cause soap scum to form on clothes, dishes, and skin. It can cause scaly deposits to build up in pipes and water heaters.**

Unit 6
FOOD CHEMISTRY

LESSON
29

FOOD CHEMISTRY

YOU ARE WHAT YOU EAT

SUPPLY LIST

Ingredients to make your favorite cookies

Supplies for Challenge: Research materials on food chemicals   Copy of "Food Chemicals" worksheet

WHAT DID WE LEARN?

- What are the three main types of chemicals that naturally occur in food? **Carbohydrates, proteins, and fats.**
- What kinds of chemicals are often added to foods? **Preservatives, flavor enhancers, and color enhancers.**
- Why is the kitchen a great place to look for chemicals? **All of our foods are made of chemicals, and many chemical reactions occur as we are cooking.**

TAKING IT FURTHER

- If you eat a peanut butter and jelly sandwich, which part of the sandwich will be providing the most carbohydrates? The most fat? The most protein? **The bread will provide the most carbohydrates, although it depends on how much jelly you put on. Jelly is mostly sugar, which is also a carbohydrate. The peanut butter will provide nearly all of the fat and most of the protein.**

CHALLENGE: FOOD CHEMICALS WORKSHEET

1. What chemical is found in coffee and soft drinks that interferes with some people falling asleep? **Caffeine.**
2. What is the chemical name for table sugar? **Sucrose.**
3. What is the chemical name for baking soda? **Sodium bicarbonate.**
4. What is the chemical name for table salt? **Sodium chloride.**
5. What chemical makes you cry when you slice onions? **Sulfuric acid.**
6. What chemical gives peppers their hot flavor? **Capsaicin.**
7. What chemical gives carrots their orange color? **Carotene.**
8. What chemical gives tomatoes their red color? **Lycopene.**
9. What chemical gives broccoli its green color? **Chlorophyll.**
10. What chemical gives soda pop its bubbles? **Carbon dioxide.**

MATTER

LESSON 30

CHEMICAL ANALYSIS OF FOOD

HOW DO I KNOW WHAT I'M EATING?

SUPPLY LIST

Copy of "Chemical Analysis" worksheet   Iodine   Potato or tortilla chips   Apple slices
Brown paper bag   Bread   Flour   Vegetable oil   Peanut butter
Supplies for Challenge: Copy of "How Many Calories Did I Eat?" worksheet
Copy of "Calories Chart"

CHEMICAL ANALYSIS WORKSHEET

- **Foods with oil: vegetable oil, peanut butter, chips. Foods with starch: bread, flour. An apple does not contain fat/oil or starch.**

WHAT DID WE LEARN?

- What are the main chemicals listed on food labels? **Carbohydrates such as sugar and starch, proteins, fats, vitamins, and minerals.**

- How do food manufacturers know what to put on their labels? **Chemists have tested the foods to see what they are composed of.**

- What is one way to test if a food contains oil? **Place a sample on brown paper for a few minutes and see if it makes the paper become translucent.**

- What is an indicator? **A substance that is used to detect the presence of a particular chemical, usually by changing color.**

TAKING IT FURTHER

- How do you suppose indicators work? **Usually the indicator molecules react with the desired chemical to produce a substance that is a different color from the indicator. For example, iodine turns blue in the presence of starch molecules because of a chemical reaction with the starch that produces a blue substance.**

- Why is it important to know what chemicals are in our food? **This information allows us to compare different foods and decide which ones are best to eat. Also, some people are allergic to particular foods and food labels help them avoid those foods.**

LESSON 31

FLAVORS

CHOCOLATE OR VANILLA?

SUPPLY LIST

Instant pudding mix (your favorite flavor)   Milk
Supplies for Challenge: Roll of Life Savers candies

What did we learn?

- What two parts of your body are needed in order to fully enjoy the flavor of your food? **The taste buds in your mouth and the smell receptors in your nose.**

- What is the difference between an herb and a spice? **Herbs come from the leaves of a plant; spices come from other parts of the plant.**

- What is the difference between a natural flavor and an artificial flavor? **Natural flavors come directly from a plant. Artificial flavors are created by combining chemicals in a lab or factory.**

Taking it further

- Why might a cook prefer to use fresh herbs rather than dried herbs? **Fresh herbs usually have a milder flavor than dried herbs. However, fresh herbs can spoil more quickly than dried herbs.**

- Why do you think artificial vanilla tastes different than natural vanilla even though they may have the same chemical formula? **Flavor is a complicated thing. Scientists are not quite sure how the flavors are changed, but artificial flavors often produce an unpleasant or bitter aftertaste that natural flavors do not have.**

LESSON

32 Additives

What's really in your food?

Supply list

Apple   Lemon juice

Supplies for Challenge: Copy of "Food Additives Checklist" worksheet

What did we learn?

- What is a food additive? **Anything that is added to the food by a manufacturer.**
- Name three different kinds of additives. **Preservatives, antioxidants, emulsifiers, stabilizers, coloring, flavor enhancers, vitamins, and minerals.**
- Why are preservatives sometimes added to foods? **To keep the foods from spoiling.**
- What compound has been used as a preservative for thousands of years? **Salt has been used to preserve many foods, especially meats. Sugar has also been used for a long time.**
- Why are emulsifiers sometimes added to foods? **To keep the oil and water in the foods from separating. Remember when you made mayonnaise?**

Taking it further

- Why are vitamins and minerals added to foods? **Processing, such as heating, often kills bacteria but also destroys many of the nutrients in the foods. Vitamins and minerals are often added back in to restore the nutritional value of the food.**

- Why does homemade bread spoil faster than store bought bread? **Because it does not contain preservatives like the store bought bread does.**

LESSON 33

BREAD

WHY IS IT LIGHT AND FLUFFY?

SUPPLY LIST

Flour   Butter or margarine   Yeast   Water   Salt   Milk   Sugar   Baking pan
Spray oil   Large bowl   Small bowl
Supplies for Challenge: Store-bought bread (with preservatives)   Plastic zipper bags
Copy of "Homemade vs. Store-bought" worksheet

WHAT DID WE LEARN?

- If you want fluffy bread, what are the two most important ingredients? **Wheat flour that contains gluten, and yeast.**

- Why is gluten important for fluffy bread? **The gluten allows the bread dough to stretch and traps the gas produced by the yeast.**

- Why does bread have to be baked before you eat it? **The baking process breaks down the long starch molecules into smaller molecules that are more easily digested.**

- Why is whole wheat bread more nutritious than white bread? **The white flour does not contain all of the parts of the wheat kernel, so it has fewer nutrients.**

TAKING IT FURTHER

- What would happen if you did not put any sugar in your bread dough? **The yeast would not be able to produce as much carbon dioxide gas, so your bread would not be as fluffy.**

- Can bread be made without yeast? **Yes, other forms of leavening can be used such as baking soda or baking powder. However, the bread will be more like tortillas or pita bread than the fluffy bread you may be used to.**

CHALLENGE: HOMEMADE VS. STORE-BOUGHT WORKSHEET

- **Homemade bread in general will dry out faster and will grow more mold than store-bought bread. However, you may prefer the flavor of homemade bread. Also, homemade bread my be more nutritious.**

QUIZ 6

FOOD CHEMISTRY

LESSONS 29–33

Use the terms below to fill in the blanks.

1. _B_ Which is the most popular drink in the world?

2. _A_ What is 70% of all soda pop sweetened with?

3. _D_ To guarantee that each can of soda tastes the same, what must a company do?

4. _D_ Which of the following is not used to make soda pop?

5. _D_ What accounts for the perceived flavor of a food?

6. _B_ Which civilization is believed to be the first to enjoy chocolate?

7. _C_ What is the purpose of fermenting vanilla beans?

8. _B_ Which of the following is a natural flavor?

9. _A_ How do additives help preserve food?

10. _C_ Which of the following helps bread to be fluffy?

11. _B_ Which agency oversees the use of food additives?

12. _C_ Which of the following makes bread easier to digest?

CHALLENGE QUESTIONS

13. _D_ Which chemical is the name for table sugar?

14. _C_ Which chemical gives tomatoes their red color?

15. _A_ A calorimeter measures energy in food by **_burning_** it.

16. _B_ Flavor is combination of **_taste and smell_**.

17. _B_ Food additives usually are not used for **_calories_**.

18. _B_ Approximately how many Calories does a teenager need each day?

LESSON 34

IDENTIFICATION OF UNKNOWN SUBSTANCES

WHAT IS THIS, ANYWAY?

FINAL PROJECT SUPPLY LIST

Copy of "Identification of Solids" worksheet   Copy of "Identification of Liquids" worksheet
Iodine   Vinegar   Baking soda   Water   Cornstarch   Rubbing alcohol
Powdered sugar   Vegetable oil

FINAL PROJECT INSTRUCTIONS

Set up each of the following experiments. Have your students write their observations on copies of the "Identification of Solids" and "Identification of Liquids" worksheets.

- **Experiment 1:** Number three plates or other containers with the numbers 1–3. On plate 1 place two tablespoons of cornstarch. On plate 2 place two tablespoons of powdered sugar. On plate 3 place two tablespoons of baking soda. Do not tell your student which substance is which until after he/she has done the experiments on the worksheet. You may give younger children a list of substances from which to choose.

- **Experiment 2:** Number three cups 1–3. Place ½ cup of water in cup 1. Place ½ cup of vinegar in cup 2. Place ½ cup of rubbing alcohol in cup 3. Again, do not tell your student which substance is which until he/she has done the experiments on the worksheet. Again, you may want to give younger children a list of possible choices.

What did we learn?

- What method should be used in identifying unknown substances? **The scientific method.**

- Why should you avoid tasting unknown substances? **The substance can be dangerous or harmful, so you don't want to taste it if you don't know what it is.**

- How can you test the scent of an unknown substance safely? **Hold it a few inches away from your nose and push some air toward your nose. This allows you to smell a few molecules without damaging your nose if the scent is very strong or caustic, like ammonia.**

- What are some physical characteristics of an unknown substance you can test at home? **Mass, density, melting point, freezing point, boiling point, and state—such as solid, liquid, or gas.**

- What are some chemical characteristics you can test at home? **Presence of starch, oil, baking powder, acid or base.**

Taking it further

- Why is it important for food manufacturers to test the ingredients they use and final products they produce? **To ensure the safety and flavor of their foods.**

- Why is it important for water treatment facilities to test the quality of the water? **We don't want harmful bacteria or other dangerous substances in our water supply.**

FINAL EXAM

PROPERTIES OF MATTER

LESSONS 1–34

Use the terms below to fill in the blanks.

1. How much of a substance you have is its _**mass**_.
2. How much space something occupies is its _**volume**_.
3. How much gravity pulls on a mass is its _**weight**_.
4. The three states of matter are _**solid**_, _**liquid**_, and _**gas**_.
5. When a liquid changes to a gas it is called _**evaporation**_.
6. When a solid changes to a liquid it is called _**melting**_.
7. When a liquid changes to a solid it is called _**freezing**_.
8. When a gas changes to a liquid it is called _**condensation**_.
9. When a solid changes directly to a gas it is called _**sublimation**_.
10. The thickness of a liquid is called its _**viscosity**_.

Match the type of quantitate measurement with the proper tool.

11. _**B**_ Volume of a liquid
12. _**D**_ Mass
13. _**C**_ Weight
14. _**E**_ Temperature

15. _A_ Volume of a cube

For each characteristic or statement, put E if it describes an element, C if it describes a compound, or M if it describes a mixture. Some statements have more than one answer.

16. Cannot be broken by ordinary chemical processes. _E_

17. Contains two or more kinds of atoms. _C, M_

18. Always has the same ratio of elements. _E, C_

19. Iron _E_

20. Water _C_

21. Helium _E_

22. Air _M_

23. Seawater _M_

24. Only 92 of these occur in nature. _E_

25. Almost all substances on earth are these. _M_

Identify each of the following changes as either a physical change (P) or a chemical change (C).

26. Burning of a candle _C_

27. Rusting metal _C_

28. Freezing of water _P_

29. Crushing a graham cracker _P_

30. Combining oxygen and hydrogen to make water _C_

31. Rain falling from the clouds _P_

Identify each characteristic as describing either a gas, a liquid, or a solid. Some statements have more than one answer.

32. Molecules are far apart. _Gas_.

33. Has a definite shape. _Solid_.

34. Easily compressed. _Gas_.

35. Takes on the shape of its container. _Liquid, gas_.

36. Molecules are very close together. _Solid, liquid_.

37. Molecules slide over one another. _Liquid_.

Short answer:

38. If a liquid is cooled will it be able to dissolve more or fewer solids? **Fewer.**

39. If a glass of soda pop is very bubbly looking is it more likely to be warm or cold? **Warm.**

40. What similar processes are required to produce the flavors of vanilla and chocolate? **Both require fermenting, aging and drying.**

41. How can you tell if a solution is saturated? **No more solute will dissolve.**

42. How can you tell if a liquid mixture is a solution or a suspension? **If it is a suspension, particles will settle on the bottom; if it is a solution, there will be no settling.**

CHALLENGE QUESTIONS

Identify each statement as origins or operational science.

43. _**Operational**_ The melting point of copper is 1084.62°C (1984.32°F).

44. _**Origins**_ All birds had a common reptile ancestor.

45. _**Operational**_ Horses give birth to horses.

46. List three different scales used to measure different kinds of storms. **Beaufort—wind; Fujita—tornado; Saffir-Simpson—hurricane**

Mark each statement as either True or False.

47. _**F**_ An object is denser than another object if it has a greater volume.

48. _**F**_ Rubbing alcohol is buoyant in water.

49. _**T**_ Solid water is less dense than liquid water.

50. _**T**_ Dissolving salt in water is a physical change.

51. _**T**_ During diffusion, molecules move from an area of higher concentration to an area of lower concentration.

52. _**F**_ A native mineral has two kinds of elements in it.

53. _**T**_ Chromatography uses paper to separate substances in a mixture.

54. _**T**_ Enzymes are used to harden cheese curds.

55. _**F**_ A centrifuge uses evaporation to separate substances in a mixture.

Match each word with its definition.

56. _**C**_ Amount of salt in a solution

57. _**D**_ Water containing calcium and magnesium

58. _**F**_ Energy to raise 1g of water 1 degree C.

59. _**E**_ 1000 calories (kilocalorie)

60. _**B**_ Flavor enhancer

61. _**A**_ Prevents reacting with oxygen

LESSON 35

CONCLUSION

A RELIABLE WORLD

SUPPLY LIST

2 balloons   Water   Candle   Matches or lighter

WHAT DID WE LEARN?

- What is the best thing you learned about matter? **Answers will vary.**

TAKING IT FURTHER

- What else would you like to know about matter? **Go to the library and learn about it.**

Properties of Ecosystems

ECOSYSTEMS

INTRODUCTION TO ECOSYSTEMS

LESSON 1

WHAT IS AN ECOSYSTEM?

BIOMES

SUPPLY LIST

String   Yardstick/meter stick   Magnifying glass   Copy of "My Backyard Habitat" worksheet
Supplies for Challenge: Copy of "World Map"   World atlas

WHAT DID WE LEARN?

- What is ecology? **The study of plants and animals and the environment in which they live.**

- What is the biosphere? **The part of the earth in which living things exist—includes the atmosphere, surface of the earth, underground, and the water.**

- Give an example of something that is biotic and something that is abiotic. **Examples of biotic: plants, animals, fungi, bacteria. Examples of abiotic: rocks, man-made objects, soil, weather.**

- What is flora? **Plants.**

- What is fauna? **Animals.**

TAKING IT FURTHER

- What factor has the greatest effect on the plants and animals that live in a particular ecosystem? **The climate.**

- How does your habitat change throughout the day? **Moving from the home to school or a store, going to the park or other area of activity.**

- List some ways that climate affects the habitats of people. **The houses they live in, the clothes they wear, the activities they participate in, and the foods that are readily available.**

LESSON

2

NICHES

WHAT'S YOUR JOB?

SUPPLY LIST

Jar   Dark soil   Sand   Oats   Earthworms   Dark construction paper   Tape
3-ring binder   9 dividers for the notebook

WHAT DID WE LEARN?

- What is a niche? **The roles played by the plant or animal within its environment.**

- Name two factors that determine an animal's niche. **What it eats, what eats it, how it acts, things it can do, and its relationships with other animals.**

- What is a population? **The total number of a single species in a given area.**

- What is a community? **All of the populations in a given area.**

- What are two different kinds of niches an animal can have? **The niche a species has within the whole community and the niche a particular organism has within its species/colony.**

TAKING IT FURTHER

- What different niches do you fill in your family and in your community? **Child, sibling, cook, student, team member, performer, etc.**

- How does competition for food and other resources affect the niche of a plant or animal? **Competition occurs when there are limited resources. This limits the population of a species. It may result in certain plants or animals being aggressive or having specialized roles.**

CHALLENGE: WHAT'S MY NICHE?

The following lists are not exhaustive; there are many other possible answers:

- Tree: **A tree serves many purposes. It is a home to many animals such as birds, squirrels, and insects. It provides shade and protection. The tree adds oxygen to the air and makes food for many animals when it performs photosynthesis. Some trees provide food through their leaves, fruit, and seeds. Trees hold the soil with their roots and draw water up from underground. They use some water for photosynthesis and release other water into the air.**

- Robin: **A robin eats insects and seeds and uses materials in its area to build its nest. Sometimes a robin becomes food for other animals such as cats or coyotes. Robins migrate so they provide these functions in different areas at different times. Robins sing which not only pleases people, but attracts a mate or drives away competitors. The robin's droppings help fertilize the ground helping new plants to grow.**

- Mouse: **A mouse eats plants and small insects. It builds its home in many different areas including underground, in hollows of a tree, in buildings, and more. Mice chew up nearly any available material to make their nests. Mice become food for many animals such as owls and snakes. Mice also become the home of fleas and other small insects. Mice can be carriers of diseases. Their droppings also help fertilize the ground.**

- Wolf: **A wolf moves over a large area of land so it affects many plants and animals. It is a predator that eats many smaller animals including rabbits, prairie dogs, fish, and even mice. Packs of wolves often attack larger animals such as deer and elk. It makes its home in burrows and may become a nuisance to farmers and ranchers.**

- Grass—**Grass is found in nearly every part of the world. It serves many roles. It performs photosynthesis so it removes carbon dioxide from the air and adds oxygen to the air. Its leaves, seeds, and roots provide food for many different animals from deer and elk to wildebeests and elephants. Grass can also be a decorative part of a person's yard.**

LESSON 3

FOOD CHAINS

DOES IT HAVE LINKS?

SUPPLY LIST

Drawing materials

WHAT DID WE LEARN?

- What is a food chain? **A series of organisms in the order in which they feed on one another.**
- What is a producer? **A plant—something that makes its own food.**
- What is a consumer? **An organism that feeds on other organisms.**
- What is a food web? **Interconnecting food chains.**
- List two herbivores. **Deer, antelope, cattle, horses.**
- List two carnivores. **Wolf, coyote, weasel, lion, snake.**
- List two omnivores. **Bear, man, raccoon, mice.**

TAKING IT FURTHER

- Is a black bear a first or second order consumer? **It depends on what it is eating. If it is eating plants, it is a first order consumer. If it is eating fish, it is a second or maybe even third order consumer, depending on what the fish ate.**
- Is man an herbivore, carnivore, or omnivore? **Some people choose to live a vegetarian lifestyle, so they would be considered herbivores, but most people eat producers and consumers and would be considered omnivores.**
- Explain how a food chain shows energy flow. **A food chain starts with a plant, which converts sunlight into energy. That energy is passed on to the animal that eats the plant. Some of that energy is used up and some becomes part of the animal's body. That energy is then passed on to the next consumer.**

LESSON 4

SCAVENGERS & DECOMPOSERS

BREAKING IT DOWN

SUPPLY LIST

Food chain and food web pictures from lesson 3
Supplies for Challenge: Drawing materials

WHAT DID WE LEARN?

- What type of organisms eat dead plants and animals? **Scavengers.**

- Name two different animals that eat dead plants or animals? **Vultures, flies, earthworms, coyotes, opossums, etc.**

- What types of organisms are at the end of every food chain? **Decomposers.**

- Name two common organisms responsible for decomposition. **Bacteria and fungi.**

TAKING IT FURTHER

- Why is decomposition so important? **It is the process that frees up the elements that were stored in the tissues of the dead plant or animal so they can be recycled.**

- What physical law makes decomposition necessary? **The law of conservation of matter/mass.**

RELATIONSHIPS AMONG LIVING THINGS

DEPENDING ON EACH OTHER

SUPPLY LIST

Copy of "Symbiosis" worksheet   Optional: Rock with lichen   Magnifying glass

Supplies for Challenge: Research materials on liver flukes   Drawing materials

SYMBIOSIS WORKSHEET

- Illustrate which species benefits, which is unaffected, and which is harmed in each relationship by filling in the chart with the following types of symbiosis.

		Species B	
	+	**0**	**–**
Species A **+**	Mutualism	Commensalism	Parasitism
0	Commensalism	Neutralism	XXX
–	Parasitism	XXX	Competition

WHAT DID WE LEARN?

- What is symbiosis? **A close relationship between two different species.**

- What is mutualism? **A symbiotic relationship in which both species benefit from each other.**

- What happens to each species in a parasitic relationship? **The guest benefits and the host is harmed.**

- Which species benefits in commensalism? **The host species benefits.**

- What is competition among species? **When two species compete for limited resources.**

- What is the name of a relationship in which neither species benefits nor is harmed? **Neutralism.**

TAKING IT FURTHER

- Why is competition considered harmful for both species? **When their resources are limited some plants or animals will not get what they need and may die or fail to reproduce. This could affect both species that are competing for the resources.**

- Explain how competition could keep the species from becoming too populated. **When there are not enough resources for everyone to live, some plants or animals will die or fail to reproduce. This will prevent the population from becoming too large.**

CHALLENGE: LIVER FLUKES

- **The sheep liver fluke enters a sheep when it eats grass containing fluke larvae. The larvae enter the sheep's liver and mature. Inside the liver the mature flukes lay eggs which then move into the sheep's digestive system and then into the feces and leave the sheep. The eggs enter water where they are eaten by certain snails. Inside the snail the fluke reproduces. These new larvae leave the snail and swim to grass. On the grass the larvae lose their tails and form cysts which climb up the grass and wait to be eaten by sheep. Other flukes have similar life cycles which require multiple hosts.**

- **There is a parasitic relationship between the fluke and the sheep and between the fluke and the snail. There is commensalism between the fluke and the grass.**

LESSON 6
OXYGEN & WATER CYCLES
WHAT COMES AROUND GOES AROUND

SUPPLY LIST

Potting soil   Glass jar with lid   Grass or other plant   Camera or drawing materials

Supplies for Challenge: Research materials on the nitrogen cycle

WHAT DID WE LEARN?

- How do photosynthesis and respiration demonstrate the oxygen cycle? **During photosynthesis carbon dioxide and water, which contain oxygen atoms, are absorbed. Glucose and oxygen are produced. Animals eat the glucose and breathe in the oxygen. During respiration these molecules are broken down to release the energy and to produce water and carbon dioxide for plants to use again.**

- What are the major steps in the water cycle? **Evaporation, condensation, and precipitation.**

TAKING IT FURTHER

- Water exists in three forms: solid, liquid and gas. What phase is the water in before and after evaporation? **It changes from liquid into gas.**

- What phase is the water in before and after condensation? **It changes from gas to liquid.**

- What phase is the water in before and after precipitation? **If the temperature is not too cold it stays as a liquid. If the temperature is cold enough the water can change from liquid to solid and comes down as snow or sleet.**

QUIZ 1 · INTRODUCTION TO ECOSYSTEMS

LESSONS 1–6

Match the term to its definition.

1. _N_ Decomposer
2. _D_ Biotic
3. _B_ Ecology
4. _L_ Omnivore
5. _E_ Abiotic
6. _F_ Ecosystem/biome
7. _K_ Carnivore
8. _C_ Biosphere
9. _G_ Flora
10. _I_ Niche
11. _H_ Fauna
12. _A_ Habitat
13. _J_ Herbivore
14. _M_ Scavenger

15. Draw a food chain with at least three levels. Label the role of each organism (producer, consumer, etc.) **Accept reasonable answers.**

16. Draw a food web with at least six organisms. **Accept reasonable answers.**

Describe each of the following relationships.

17. Mutualism: **Relationship in which both species benefit.**

18. Parasitism: **Relationship in which one species benefits and the other is harmed.**

CHALLENGE QUESTIONS

Short answer:

19. Why do animals generally not migrate from one biogeographic realm to another? **Biogeographical realms are separated by large natural barriers such as oceans, high mountains, or large deserts.**

20. Describe the niche of a butterfly. **As a larva the butterfly eats plants, its droppings fertilize plants, it uses the plants for shelter and for a place to make its chrysalis. Adult butterflies drink nectar and pollinate different plants. Butterflies provide food for birds and other animals and provide beauty for people to enjoy.**

21. What is carrying capacity? **Carrying capacity is the maximum population an area can support.**

22. How does the number of first order consumers in a given area compare to the number of second order consumers? **There must be significantly more first order consumers than second order consumers. A good rule of thumb is 10 to 1.**

23. What law makes the oxygen, water, and nitrogen cycles necessary? **Law of conservation of mass/matter**

Unit 2
Grasslands & Forests

LESSON 7
Biomes around the World
Where are they located?

Supply list

World atlas showing temperature and rainfall for the world as well as location of various ecosystems
Copies of the blank Average Rainfall, Average Temperature, and Biomes world maps
Supplies for Challenge: Research materials on ecological succession   Poster board
Drawing materials

What did we learn?

- Where is the tropical zone located? **Between the Tropic of Cancer (23.5° north latitude) and the Tropic of Capricorn (23.5° south latitude), centered on the equator.**
- Where is the northern temperate zone located? **Between the Tropic of Cancer and the Arctic Circle (66.5° N).**
- Where is the southern temperate zone located? **Between the Tropic of Capricorn and the Antarctic Circle (66.5° S).**
- Where are the polar regions located? **North of the Arctic Circle and south of the Antarctic Circle.**

Taking it further

- Why are the polar regions generally colder than the tropical regions even though they receive many more hours of sunlight each day during the summer? **The sunlight reaches the earth at a sharper angle and much of it reflects away from the surface of the earth. Also, snow and ice tend to reflect much of the sunlight rather than absorbing it, thus keeping the temperature colder.**
- What correlations do you see between the temperature and rainfall maps that you made? **Answers will vary, but there is generally more rainfall in warmer areas, excepting deserts.**

LESSON 8
Grasslands
Swaying in the breeze

Supply list

Grasses growing in a natural area   Flowering plants field guide   Newspaper   Heavy books
Cardstock or heavy paper   Page protectors   Copy of "Grasslands" summary worksheet

Supplies for Challenge: Grass plants   Scissors   Ruler   Copy of "Growing Grass" worksheet

WHAT DID WE LEARN?

- Name three characteristics of a grassland biome. **10–30 inches of rain per year, distinct wet and dry seasons, warm summers and cold winters, and grass is the primary plant with few trees and shrubs.**

- What are four different types of grasslands? **Prairie, savannah, pampas, and steppe.**

- Where can each of these grasslands be found? **Prairie—North America,; Savannah—Africa; Pampas—South America; Steppe—Europe and Asia.**

TAKING IT FURTHER

- Why are there few trees in a grassland? **There is not enough rain to support trees. Also, periodic fires kill trees and shrubs.**

- How do many plants survive extended periods of drought in the grassland? **Many plants, such as grass, become dormant until there is enough water to resume growth. Other plants have very long roots to reach water deep underground.**

- How can grass survive when it is continually being cut down by grazing animals? **The growth center of grass is at the bottom of the plant, near ground level, so it can continue to grow after its top is cut off.**

CHALLENGE: GROWING GRASS WORKSHEET

- How did cutting the grass affect its ability to grow? **It didn't.**

- Did one plant grow more than the others? **Answers will vary.**

- How does this experiment demonstrate God's provision for grassland animals? **Grass provides food for grazing animals, and continues to provide more food even when eaten over and over again.**

LESSON
9

FORESTS

FILLED WITH TREES

SUPPLY LIST

Copy of "Where Would I Live?" worksheet
Supplies for Challenge: Drawing materials

WHERE WOULD I LIVE? WORKSHEET

Emergent Layer	**Bald eagle, flies**
Canopy	**Spider monkey, opossum, fruit bat, tree frog, lemur, flies, woodpecker**
Understory	**Fruit bat, hummingbird, tree frog, flies, woodpecker**
Shrub Layer	**Monarch butterfly, hummingbird, flies**
Herb Layer	**Monarch butterfly, hummingbird, flies**
Floor	**Termites, black bear, rabbit, ibis, deer, flies**

WHAT DID WE LEARN?

- What are the major plants in a forest? **Trees.**

- What are the six layers of a forest? **Emergent layer, canopy, understory, shrub, herb, and floor.**
- Which layer forms the roof of the forest? **Canopy.**
- Name three kinds of forests. **Deciduous, coniferous, tropical rainforest.**

TAKING IT FURTHER

- Why is the forest floor relatively dark? **The trees grow close enough together for their leaves to block out much of the light.**
- Why is it important to study each layer of a forest? **Different plants and animals can be found in each layer so you must study all the layers in order to understand the whole ecosystem.**
- How might new trees find room to grow in a mature forest? **Room is made when older trees die and fall down or when trees are damaged in a storm. Also, trees can be cut down by people.**

LESSON 10 · TEMPERATE FORESTS

CAN YOU SEE THE FOREST FOR THE TREES?

SUPPLY LIST

Copy of "Deciduous Forest" and "Coniferous Forest" summary worksheets
Copy of "Tree Identification" worksheet
Supplies for Challenge: Copy of "Forest Jeopardy" worksheet

WHAT DID WE LEARN?

- What are some characteristics of a deciduous forest? **Dominant plants are deciduous trees, 30–60 inches of rainfall per year, 4 distinct seasons, warm wet summer and cold winter, trees lose leaves in the fall.**
- What are some characteristics of a coniferous forest? **Dominant plants are evergreen/coniferous trees, 12–33 inches of rainfall/precipitation per year, cold winters, many lakes.**
- What is another name for a coniferous forest in the far north? **Boreal forest or taiga.**
- What is a deciduous tree? **One that has broad flat leaves and sheds its leaves in the fall.**
- What is a coniferous tree? **One that has needle-like leaves that do not fall off and has cones instead of flowers.**

TAKING IT FURTHER

- What are some ways that plants in temperate forests were designed to withstand the cold winters? **Deciduous trees lose their leaves;, coniferous trees have needles that are not damaged by freezing temperatures. Trees have thick bark which helps protect them from cold wind and snow.**
- What are some ways that animals in temperate forests were designed to withstand the cold winters? **Many animals hibernate; others go into a deep sleep. Still others migrate to warmer areas during the winter and return in the summer months.**
- Would you expect plant material that falls to the floor of the coniferous forest to decay quickly or slowly? Why? **The floor of the coniferous forest is relatively dry and often cold. This is not an ideal environment for bacteria to grow so material decays relatively slowly in the coniferous forest.**

CHALLENGE: FOREST JEOPARDY WORKSHEET

Accept all reasonable questions.

1. Oak, maple, and beech. **What kind of trees might you find in a deciduous forest?**
2. Roof of the forest. **What is another name for the canopy of the forest?**
3. Lichen, moss, and fungi. **What plants might you find growing on the floor of a forest?**
4. Shrub layer. **What layer in the forest is below the understory?**
5. 30–60 inches per year. **How much rain does a deciduous forest receive each year?**
6. 12–33 inches per year. **How much rain/precipitation does a coniferous forest receive each year?**
7. Tropical and polar regions. **Between which two regions do you find temperate forests?**
8. Boreal forest and Taiga. **What other names refer to a coniferous forest?**
9. Dall and big horn sheep. **What are some animals that are likely to live in a coniferous forest?**
10. Many lakes. **What geologic features are found in coniferous forests as a result of the glacier movement during the Ice Age?**
11. Duck-billed platypus. **What is one animal that is found only in the forests of Australia?**
12. Tallest trees of the forest. **What would you see in the emergent layer of the forest?**

LESSON 11

TROPICAL RAINFORESTS

GROWING WHERE IT'S WET

SUPPLY LIST

Copy of "Tropical Rainforest" summary worksheet   Research materials

WHAT DID WE LEARN?

- List some ways in which a tropical rainforest is different from a temperate forest. **Rainforest receives more rain (over 80 inches per year). Rainforest is always warm to hot—no cold winters. Rainforests have more different kinds of animals, but relatively fewer mammals.**

- Where are the rainforests located? **Between the Tropic of Cancer and the Tropic of Capricorn; in the tropical region.**

- What is an arboreal animal? **One that lives primarily in trees.**

- What is an epiphyte? **A plant that grows on another plant without taking nutrients from it.**

- Name at least one epiphyte. **Orchid, fern, cactus, banyan tree.**

TAKING IT FURTHER

- Do you think that dead materials would decay slowly or quickly on the floor of the rainforest? Why? **Because the rainforest is warm and moist all the time, bacteria and other composters thrive, thus, dead material decays very quickly.**

- If you transplanted trees such as orange, cacao, or papaya trees, to a deciduous forest, would you expect them to survive? Why or why not? **Many tropical plants cannot survive the cold winters that are experienced in the deciduous forests. These plants would not be likely to survive.**

- Which animals are you most likely to see if you are taking a walk through the tropical rainforest? **Because many animals live primarily in the canopy, you would only see the ones that live near the floor or that visit the floor regularly. These might include lizards and snakes, capybaras, a few birds, and lots of insects. You would probably not see monkeys except from afar.**

QUIZ 2
GRASSLANDS & FORESTS
LESSONS 7–11

Mark each statement as either True or False.

1. _T_ A puddle of water could be considered an ecosystem.
2. _T_ The amount of sunlight hitting the earth is affected by the tilt of the earth.
3. _F_ Polar regions are near the equator.
4. _F_ It is uncommon to have a fire in a grassland.
5. _T_ Grazing animals are specially designed to eat grass.
6. _F_ Burrowing animals make it harder for grass to grow.
7. _T_ Trees are the dominant plants in a forest.
8. _F_ Temperate forests are located near the equator.
9. _T_ Arboreal animals spend most of their time in trees.
10. _F_ Epiphytes are animals that live on the forest floor.
11. _T_ Rainforests receive over 80 inches of rain each year.
12. _F_ Pampas grass is very short.
13. _T_ Tropical rainforests are located near the equator.
14. _T_ Arctic tundra is located in polar regions.
15. _T_ Rainfall and sunlight help determine the ecosystem that will develop.

Short answer:

16. Give three different names for grassland. **Pampas, savannah, prairie, steppe**
17. List the six different layers of a forest. A. **Emergent layer** B. **Canopy** C. **Understory** D. **Shrub** E. **Herb** F. **Floor**
18. List two types of trees that you are likely to find in a deciduous forest. **Oak, elm, beech.**
19. List two type of trees that you are likely to find in a coniferous forest. **Pine, fir, spruce.**
20. Name three common products that originally came from the tropical rainforest. **Avocado, pineapple, papaya, cocoa, mango, cinnamon, cloves, allspice.**

CHALLENGE QUESTIONS

21. Describe how succession might take place in a forest that was destroyed by a wildfire. **Small, quick-growing plants such as grass and dandelions will grow first. This will provide food for small animals such as rabbits and prairie dogs. These animals will attract predators such as coyotes and hawks. As the ground has more cover, there will be enough moisture for shrubs to begin to grow. The shrubs will provide habitat for nesting birds, squirrels and other animals. Tree seeds will germinate and begin to grow. Eventually, the trees**

will dominate the area again, reducing the sunlight to the floor and causing some of the smaller plants to die out. The trees will provide shelter and food for large animals such as deer and bears.

22. Explain how God designed grazing animals to survive in a grassland ecosystem. **Grazing animals have specially designed stomachs that allow them to digest grass. Different animals eat different parts of the grass plant, allowing the plant to feed more than one type of animal.**

23. Explain the purpose of each of the following parts of a tree.

    a. Outer bark: **Provides protection from hazards and harsh weather.**

    b. Phloem/inner bark: **Transports food from the leaves to rest of the plant.**

    c. Cambium: **Generates new phloem and xylem cells.**

    d. Xylem/sapwood: **Transports water and nutrients from the roots to the leaves.**

    e. Heartwood: **Provides strength and structure.**

24. Place the following ecosystems in order from least amount of rainfall to greatest amount of rainfall. **Grasslands, coniferous forest, deciduous forest, tropical rainforest.**

25. Explain the importance of the tropical rainforests on the medical field. **One-fourth of all medicines are derived from plants that come from the rainforest.**

AQUATIC ECOSYSTEMS

LESSON 12 · THE OCEAN

MARINE ECOSYSTEM

SUPPLY LIST

Copy of "Ocean" summary worksheet   Shallow pan   Water   Food coloring
Supplies for Challenge: Drawing materials

WHAT DID WE LEARN?

- How much of the earth is covered with water? **About 75%.**
- How much of the surface water of the world is in the ocean? **About 97%.**
- How many oceans are there? **Although there are 5 named oceans, they are all connected making only one ocean.**
- What are the three zones that the ocean can be divided into? **Sunlit (euphotic), twilight (disphotic), and midnight (aphotic) zones.**
- What are the three major groups of living organisms in the ocean? **Benthos, nekton, and plankton.**

TAKING IT FURTHER

- What might happen in the ocean if the currents stopped flowing? **The plankton would not be moved around and some areas of the ocean would have less food than now. This would cause some animals to die or leave the area. Nutrients in one area would be used up and plankton would die, causing other animals to die.**
- Why do most animals in the ocean live in the euphotic zone? **Photosynthesis can only take place where there is sufficient sunlight, so food is most abundant in the euphotic zone. Therefore, most animals will be found there.**
- Why might the aphotic zone occur at a shallower depth than 600 feet (200 m) in some areas? **The amount of sunlight that can penetrate the water depends on how clear the water is. If there is a significant amount of silt or other particles in the water, this will reduce the depth that the sunlight can penetrate.**

LESSON 13

CORAL REEFS

UNDERWATER WONDERLANDS

SUPPLY LIST

Copy of "Coral Reef" summary worksheet   Modeling clay

WHAT DID WE LEARN?

- Where will you find coral reefs? **In warm, clear water near the equator.**
- What is a coral reef made from? **Limestone from the exoskeletons of coral.**
- Where do corals get most of their energy? **From the algae that live with them.**
- What are the three main types of coral reefs? **Atoll, fringing, and barrier.**
- What are some of the animals that live in a coral reef besides corals? **Sponges, shrimp, sea stars, eels, turtles, octopus, fish, whales, etc.**

TAKING IT FURTHER

- Why are coral reefs found in water that is usually less than 150 feet (45 m) deep? **The algae in the coral require sunlight for photosynthesis so coral cannot survive where there is not enough sunlight.**
- Why do corals grow best in swift water? **The moving water brings more nutrients which spurs growth.**

LESSON 14

BEACHES

TAKE A WALK ON THE SAND

SUPPLY LIST

Copy of "Beach" summary worksheet   Rocks   Sea shells   Plastic zipper bag   Hammer
Safety goggles   Towel   Sand   Magnifying glass

WHAT DID WE LEARN?

- What is a beach? **The area where the water meets the land.**
- What are the two main kinds of beaches? **Rocky and sandy.**
- What is the name of the area of land that is covered at high tide and uncovered at low tide? **The intertidal zone.**
- What are some animals you are likely to see in a beach ecosystem? **Clams, mussels, crabs, oysters, starfish, barnacles, turtles, and gulls.**

TAKING IT FURTHER

- Why might you find different plants and animals on a rocky beach from those on a sandy beach? **A rocky beach provides more places for plants to anchor so a wider variety of plants and animals is likely to survive there.**

- How is new sand formed? **Waves erode rocks, shells, and coral to form new sand. Also, new sand can be formed when hot lava flows into cold water.**

- Explain how a beach can be in dynamic equilibrium. **Sand is made and deposited by the action of the waves while at the same time other sand and materials are dragged out to sea by the tide. If the amount deposited is about equal to the amount removed, the beach is said to be in dynamic equilibrium.**

LESSON 15

ESTUARIES

WHERE FRESH AND SALTY MEET

SUPPLY LIST

Copy of "Estuary" summary worksheet   4 clear cups   Water   Salt   Eyedropper
Marker   Green and blue food coloring

WHAT DID WE LEARN?

- What is an estuary? **An area where fresh water flows into saltwater.**

- Name three types of estuaries. **Salt marsh, salt meadow, and mangrove forest.**

- What are some plants you might find in an estuary? **Reeds, salt grass, mangrove trees.**

- Name several animals that you might find in an estuary. **Mud snails, marine worms, shellfish, mullet, flounder, sole, herons, terns, storks, pelicans, and sea lions.**

TAKING IT FURTHER

- Why is an estuary a very productive ecosystem? **The moving water stirs up nutrients that spur plant growth.**

- How do mangrove trees help coral reefs? **The trees help to filter out silt that might otherwise make the water cloudy.**

- Why is the salt level in the water constantly changing in an estuary? **Fresh water and saltwater do not easily mix. There is a constant flow of fresh water and a changing flow of saltwater due to tides so the salt level is changing. Seasonal changes in weather also affect salt levels.**

- Why might you find different animals in the same location at different times of the year? **Many animals migrate and spend different parts of the year in different locations.**

ECOSYSTEMS

LESSON 16

LAKES & PONDS

IT'S FRESH

SUPPLY LIST

Copy of "Lakes & Ponds" summary worksheet   2 clear cups   Water   Salt   Thermometer
Marker   Copy of "Watching Water Freeze" worksheet
Supplies for Challenge: Copy of "Great Lakes Fact Sheet"

WHAT DID WE LEARN?

- What is a lake? **A large body of fresh water.**

- What is a pond? **A lake that is not deep enough to have a dark zone.**

- What are two ways that lakes were formed in the past? **Some lakes were dug out by glaciers; others have formed in craters of extinct volcanoes. It is likely that many of the lakes formed as a result of the Great Flood.**

- What is an overturn? **It is when colder water on the top of a lake rapidly sinks causing warmer water to rise.**

- What is an algae bloom? **A rapid growth in algae.**

TAKING IT FURTHER

- Why is overturn important to lake ecosystems? **It releases nutrients and oxygen that become trapped in the mud at the bottom of the lake.**

- Why does an algae bloom often occur in a lake in the spring? **Overturn occurs in the spring and releases nutrients that algae need to grow, causing algae to grow quickly.**

- In which lake zone would you expect to find most small creatures like rotifers? **They will most likely be in the sunlit zone because they eat algae, and algae need sunlight.**

- What would happen to fish during the winter if ice did not float? **As ice began to fill up the bottom of the lake, the fish would be forced to move up in the lake. Eventually the whole lake could freeze and the fish would die.**

CHALLENGE: GREAT LAKES FACT SHEET

Answers may vary depending on the source. These numbers are from the EPA.

Feature	Lake Superior	Lake Michigan	Lake Huron	Lake Erie	Lake Ontario
Average Depth	**483 feet** **147 meters**	**279 feet** **85 meters**	**195 feet** **59 meters**	**62 feet** **19 meters**	**283 feet** **86 meters**
Maximum Depth	**1322 feet** **406 meters**	**925 feet** **282 meters**	**750 feet** **229 meters**	**210 feet** **64 meters**	**802 feet** **244 meters**
Volume	**2900 miles³** **12,100 km³**	**1180 miles³** **4920 km³**	**850 miles³** **3540 km³**	**116 miles³** **484 km³**	**393 miles³** **1640 km³**
Major cities that border it	**Duluth, MN** **Sault Ste. Marie, ON** **Thunder Bay, ON** **Marquette, MI**	**Chicago, IL** **Gary, IN** **Green Bay, WI** **Milwaukee, WI**	**Sarnia, ON** **Port Huron, MI** **Bay City, MI**	**Buffalo, NY** **Cleveland, OH** **Erie, PA** **Toledo, OH**	**Hamilton, ON** **Kingston, ON** **Oshawa, ON** **Rochester, NY** **Toronto, ON** **Mississauga, ON**

ECOSYSTEMS

RIVERS & STREAMS

FLOWING WATER

SUPPLY LIST

Copy of "Rivers & Streams" summary worksheet   Copy of "Rivers of the World" map
World atlas
Supplies for Challenge: Copy of "Rivers Fact Sheet"

WHAT DID WE LEARN?

- What is a river? **A moving body of fresh water.**

- Where does most of the energy for a river ecosystem come from? **Plant material that falls into the river.**

- Name some plants you might find in a river ecosystem. **Grasses, pussy willows, alders, elkslip, and willow trees.**

- What is a tributary? **A smaller river or stream that flows into a larger river.**

- What is the riparian zone? **The area along the banks of a river.**

TAKING IT FURTHER

- Why do fewer plants grow in the water of a river than in a lake or ocean? **The current of the river makes it difficult for plants to stay in one place, and most plants need to stay anchored to survive.**

- Would you expect a river to be larger at a higher elevation or a lower elevation? **In general, because tributaries are adding water to a river as it flows downhill, you would expect the river to be smaller at higher elevations and larger at lower elevations.**

- Do rivers move faster over steep ground or in relatively flat areas? **Gravity is what causes water to flow, so water will flow faster over steeper ground.**

- Would you expect water to cause more erosion in a steep area or in a relatively flat area? **The faster water is moving, the more erosion it can cause, so more erosion will occur in steeper areas.**

CHALLENGE: RIVERS FACT SHEET

River	Length	Size of river basin	Discharge at mouth	Countries or states it flows through	Major tributaries
Amazon	**3920 mi 6308 km**	**2,270,000 sq. mi 7,050,000 sq. km**	**219,000 cu. meters/sec.**	**Peru, Brazil, Columbia, Venezuela, Bolivia**	**Negro, Tocantins**
Congo	**2900 mi 4700 km**	**1,440,000 sq. mi 3,822,000 sq. km**	**42,000 cu. meters/sec.**	**African Republic, Republic of the Congo, Angola, Zambia, Tanzania**	**Ubangi River, Aruwimi, Kasai, Lomami**
Nile	**4180 mi 6727 km**	**1,312,000 sq. mi 3,40,000 sq. km**	**2830 cu. meters/sec.**	**Ethiopia, Sudan, Egypt, Rwanda, Tanzania, Uganda, Burundi, Dem, Rep. of Congo, Eritrea, Kenya**	**White Nile, Blue Nile**

Mississippi	2320 mi 3734 km	1,151,000 sq. mi 2,981,000 sq. km	12,743 cu. meters/sec.	USA: MN, WI, IA, IL, MO, KY, TN, AR, LA, MS	Ohio, Missouri, Arkansas, Tennessee
Yangtze	3964 mi 6379 km	680,000 sq. mi 1,970,000 sq. km	35,000 cu. meters/sec.	China	Yalong, Minjiang, Jialing, Tuo he, Han
Rio De La Plata	2795 mi 4500 km	1,197,000 sq. mi 3,100,000 sq. km	17,100 cu. meters/sec.	Argentina, Uraguay	Paraguay, Pilcomayo, Parana, Uraguay
Hwang Ho/ Yellow	3395 mi 5464 km	290,000 sq. mi 745,000 sq. km	2,571 cu. meters/sec.	China	White, Black, Huang River
Orinoco	1300 mi 2100 km	340,000 sq. mi 880,000 sq. km	33,000 cu. meters/sec.	Venezuela, Brazil	Apure, Caura, Caroni
Yukon	2200 mi 3685 km	330,000 sq. mi 855,000 sq. km	6,430 cu. meters/sec.	United States (Alaska), Canada	Pelly, Porcupine Tanana
Volga	2290 mi 3688 km	533,000 sq. mi 1,380,000 sq. km	8,000 cu. meters/sec.	Russia	Kama, Oka, Moskva

QUIZ 3

AQUATIC ECOSYSTEMS

LESSONS 12–17

ECOSYSTEMS

Write the correct term from the list below in each blank. Not all terms are used.

1. _Phytoplankton_ is microscopic aquatic organisms that perform photosynthesis.

2. Plants and animals that live on the ocean floor are called _benthos_.

3. An _atoll_ is a coral reef formed around a sunken volcano.

4. _Nekton_ are animals that freely move throughout the ocean.

5. Where the ocean meets the land is called a _beach_.

6. An ecosystem where fresh water flows into the ocean is called an _estuary_.

7. Sudden rapid growth of algae is called an _algae bloom_.

8. Land along the banks of a river or stream is the _riparian zone_.

9. A _tributary_ is a smaller stream or river that flows into a larger stream or river.

10. The _inter-tidal zone_ is the part of the shore that is covered with water at high tide and uncovered at low tide.

11. A lake that is too shallow to have an aphotic zone is referred to as a _pond_.

12. A coral reef attached to land is a _fringing reef_.

13. _Plankton_ are plants and animals that move with the ocean currents.

14. The layer of water that sunlight is able to penetrate is the _sunlit/euphotic zone_.

15. _Overturn_ is the rapid exchange of cold and warm-water regions within a lake.

Short answer:

16. Briefly explain why you can expect to find more varieties of plants on a rocky beach than on a sandy beach. **Rocky beaches provide more cracks and soil for plants to anchor to.**

17. Why do coral grow only in relatively shallow water? **Coral rely on algae in their tissues to produce food for them. This requires sunlight for photosynthesis, so coral only grow where there is abundant sunlight.**

18. What is overturn in a lake? **Overturn is the rapid movement of cold water layers to the bottom of a lake and warm layers of water to the top of a lake.**

19. Why is an estuary a very productive ecosystem? **The water currents stir up and bring in a large amount of nutrients that spur plant growth.**

20. Which organisms form the base of the food chain in the ocean? **Plankton, particularly phytoplankton, produce most of the food that forms the base of the food chains in the ocean.**

CHALLENGE QUESTIONS

Mark each statement as either True or False.

21. _T_ Bioluminescent creatures produce light through a chemical reaction.

22. _F_ Coral bleaching occurs when there is too much bleach in the water.

23. _F_ Coral bleaching always causes the coral to die.

24. _T_ Algae and coral have a symbiotic relationship.

25. _T_ A dune system is an example of ecological succession.

26. _F_ A maritime forest usually has large trees.

27. _T_ The grass in a dune system helps to stabilize the dunes.

28. _T_ Dune grass must be tolerant to salt and wind.

29. _F_ Land can only be part of a single watershed.

30. _T_ The Mississippi River Basin is the largest watershed in the United States.

31. _F_ Water from the Mississippi River mixes quickly with the Gulf of Mexico.

32. _T_ The Great Lakes provide water and work for over 35 million people.

33. _F_ Invasive species are not a real threat to animals in the Great Lakes.

34. _T_ The Great Lakes can generate their own weather systems.

35. _F_ The Mississippi River has the largest volume of any river.

36. _T_ The Nile River is one of the longest rivers in the world.

37. _T_ River ecosystems vary as the speed of the river changes.

38. _T_ The Volga River is an important ecosystem in Russia.

39. _T_ The Amazon River has the largest watershed in the world.

40. _F_ Bioluminescent creatures live primarily in the sunlit zone.

ECOSYSTEMS

EXTREME ECOSYSTEMS

LESSON 18

TUNDRA

IS IT FROZEN?

SUPPLY LIST

Copy of "Tundra" summary worksheet   Small box   White cotton balls   Large bowl
White tissue paper or white quilt batting   Photos of Arctic animals with white fur or feathers
Two pairs of gloves (one pair must fit inside the other, for example one could be cotton gardening gloves and the other could be leather work gloves)   Ice

WHAT DID WE LEARN?

- Where is most tundra located? **In the northern regions of Alaska, Canada, Greenland, Scandinavia, and Russia.**

- What is permafrost? **The layer below the surface that never thaws, even in summer.**

- What kind of plants grow in the tundra? **Small plants, including: flowers, small shrubs, rushes, sedges, heather, mosses, and lichens.**

- What are some animals you might find in the tundra? **Polar bears, Arctic foxes, caribou, moose, ptarmigan, Canada geese, Arctic hares, flies, and mosquitoes.**

- How much precipitation does the tundra receive? **6–10 inches a year.**

TAKING IT FURTHER

- Why do many animals in the tundra have white fur or feathers? **To provide them with camouflage from predators in the snow.**

- Why do many animals and plants have an accelerated life cycle in the tundra? **Because the growing season is only 50–60 days long.**

- Why do you think the temperatures are so cool in the summer when there is often 24 hours of sunshine? **Although the sun is up for many weeks, its light reaches the earth at a steep angle in the tundra so the energy is spread out. Also, the ice and snow reflect much of the light away from the ground, thus keeping it cool.**

LESSON 19 · DESERT
SAND AND MORE SAND

SUPPLY LIST

Copy of "Desert" summary worksheet   Thin plastic bag (such as a produce bag)

WHAT DID WE LEARN?

- What is a desert ecosystem? **One which receives less than 10 inches of rain per year.**
- How is a cold desert different from a hot desert? **Daytime temperatures drop below freezing in the winter in a cold desert but remain significantly above freezing during the day in a hot desert.**
- What are some plants you would expect to find in the desert? **Cactus, sagebrush, aloe, mesquite, Joshua tree, creosote bush, and desert trumpet.**
- What are some animals you would expect to find in the desert? **Mouse, toad, snake, lizard, badgers, ostriches, vultures, owls, and coyotes.**
- What is the difference between a Bactrian camel and a Dromedary camel? **Bactrian camels have two humps and longer hair; Dromedary camels have short hair and one hump.**

TAKING IT FURTHER

- In what ways are plants well suited for the desert environment? **Some can store large amounts of water; some have needles that do not lose water through transpiration; others have leaves with very few stomata; many have accelerated life cycles.**
- In what ways are animals well suited for the desert environment? **Most are nocturnal; some estivate; many have an accelerated life cycle.**
- Why does rain often cause flash flooding in the desert? **The ground is so dry and hard that water does not quickly soak in.**
- What are some dangers you may face in the desert? **Dehydration due to lack of water, heat stroke, freezing/exposure due to cold temperatures when the sun goes down, sand storms, and scorpion stings.**
- Why do salt flats often form in the desert? **Since water does not quickly soak into the ground, much of it evaporates, leaving dissolved salt behind. Over hundreds of years, this salt builds up to form salt flats.**
- Would you expect to find more salt flats in a cold desert or a hot desert? **More salt flats are found in cold deserts because cold deserts usually receive more water than hot deserts.**

LESSON 20 · OASES
A REFRESHING SPOT

SUPPLY LIST

Copy of "Oasis" summary worksheet   Several plant leaves   Plastic zipper bag
Supplies for Challenge: Research materials on desert products   Poster board   Drawing materials

WHAT DID WE LEARN?

- What is an oasis? **An ecosystem in the desert where water is readily available.**

- What kinds of plants grow in an oasis? **Palm trees, shrubs, grass, and cacti.**

- What kinds of animals live in an oasis that don't usually live in a desert? **Fish, bats, warblers, and orioles.**

TAKING IT FURTHER

- Why is it often cooler in an oasis than in a desert? **The transpiration from the trees results in evaporation which cools the air. Also, the leaves of the trees block some of the sun.**

- Why are oases important for trade routes? **The only way to safely cross the desert in the past was by traveling from one oasis to another.**

- How might a man-made oasis change the ecosystem in a desert? **The water that is brought in will make it possible to grow plants that do not naturally grow there. This will provide habitat for animals that do no naturally live there. Also, it will add humidity to the air, thus cooling it down and possibly increasing the rainfall.**

LESSON 21

MOUNTAINS

PURPLE MOUNTAIN MAJESTIES

SUPPLY LIST

Copy of "Mountain" summary worksheet   Art supplies   Newspaper   Paint   Leaves
Twigs   Grass   Small flowers   Cotton balls
Supplies for Challenge: Research materials on the Himalayas

WHAT DID WE LEARN?

- What ecosystems are you likely to encounter on mountains in temperate zones? **Grasslands, deciduous forests, evergreen forests, alpine meadows, and alpine tundra.**

- What ecosystems are you likely to encounter on mountains in tropical zones? **Rainforests, bamboo forests, heath, meadows, and tundra.**

- What is timberline? **The point above which no trees will grow.**

- What is snow line? **The point above which the snow does not completely melt, even in the summertime.**

TAKING IT FURTHER

- Why do the ecosystems change as you gain altitude on a mountain? **Temperature, rainfall, and oxygen levels change as you gain altitude, so different plants and animals will live at different altitudes.**

- Why don't you find every ecosystem on every mountain? **Different mountains are different heights. Most mountains are not high enough to experience all of the different ecosystems.**

- What other ecosystems are you likely to find on mountains that were not listed in the lesson? **Rivers, lakes, and ponds are abundant in most mountains.**

- How have glaciers influenced the shapes of mountains? **As glaciers receded at the end of the Great Ice Age, they dug out valleys, lakes, and other features in the mountains.**

- Why is there less oxygen as you gain altitude? **The gravitational pull of the earth becomes less as you go away from the center of the earth, so fewer air molecules are held close to the earth at higher altitudes.**

LESSON 22 · CHAPARRAL

THE MEDITERRANEAN CLIMATE

SUPPLY LIST

Copy of "Chaparral" summary worksheet   Pictures of the chaparral

WHAT DID WE LEARN?

- What is a chaparral ecosystem? **An ecosystem on hot, dry slopes in areas with mild, rainy winters.**
- What are two other names for chaparral? **Mediterranean ecosystem or maquis.**
- Name some plants you might find in the chaparral. **Scrub oak, live oak, yucca, buckbrush, and trefoil.**
- Name some animals you might find in the chaparral. **Woodrat, rabbit, fox, coyote, bobcat, quail, jay, wren, and sparrow.**
- What animal might you find in the Australian chaparral that you would not find in the American chaparral? **Koala.**

TAKING IT FURTHER

- What conditions make fire likely in the chaparral? **Hot, dry summers with low humidity, thick shrubbery, windy weather, and lightning.**
- How are plants in the chaparral specially designed for fire? **Seeds from many species only germinate after a fire.**
- Should people try to put out fires that naturally occur in the chaparral? **This is a difficult question to answer. Certainly if people's property is in danger the fires should be controlled. But studies have shown that fire is a natural part of the chaparral ecosystem and actually helps to keep it healthy, so many people think that natural fires should be allowed to burn when not endangering people or their property.**

LESSON 23 · CAVES

ARE THEY JUST HOLES IN THE GROUND?

SUPPLY LIST

Copy of "Cave" summary worksheet   Houseplant   Box
Supplies for Challenge: Drawing materials

WHAT DID WE LEARN?

- What is a cave? **A hole or cavern inside a mountain or underground.**
- What kinds of plants will you find in a cave ecosystem? **There are no plants inside the cave; a few may be growing near the entrance.**
- What are the three categories of animals in a cave ecosystem? **Trogloxenes, troglophiles, and troglobites.**

- Explain the different habits of each category of cave animal. **Trogloxenes visit the cave but do not spend their whole lives there. Troglophiles like to live in caves, but can live outside of a cave. Troglobites live their entire lives in a cave.**

- What is the main source of nutrients in a cave ecosystem? **Bat guano.**

TAKING IT FURTHER

- Why is a cave considered a low energy ecosystem? **There are no plants, so all energy must be brought in from the outside. This limits the amount of energy in the ecosystem.**

- Why can a rise in temperature inside a cave threaten the ecosystem? **Increased temperature means increased metabolism for cold-blooded animals, requiring more food, which may not be available.**

- What sense is least useful in a cave? **Sight.**

- What senses are most useful in a cave? **Hearing, smell, and touch are more useful than sight or taste.**

EXTREME ECOSYSTEMS

LESSONS 18–23

1. Place the animals below in the ecosystem(s) you are likely to find them.

Tundra	Desert	Oasis	Mountain	Cave
Arctic fox	**Toad**	**Toad**	**Arctic fox**	**Scorpions**
Reindeer	**Lizards**	**Lizards**	**Moose**	**Bats**
Moose	**Snakes**	**Snakes**	**Ground squirrel**	**Crickets**
Canada goose	**Scorpions**	**Scorpions**	**Snakes**	**Crayfish**
Ground squirrel	**Camels**	**Camels**	**Bats**	
		Bats	**Mountain lion**	
			Big horned sheep	

Choose the best answer for each statement or question.

2. _B_ The layer of permanently frozen ground in the tundra is:

3. _A_ Which do not help plants survive in the tundra?

4. _A_ On average, how much moisture does the tundra receive each year?

5. _A_ On average, how much moisture does a desert receive each year?

6. _C_ Which of the following helps animals survive in the desert?

7. _D_ Which are you not likely to find in an oasis?

8. _B_ You would expect the temperature in an oasis to be _____ than in the desert?

9. _D_ Which ecosystem would not likely be found on a mountain?

10. _A_ What is the point above which no trees will grow?

11. _C_ Which is likely to increase as you go up a mountain?

12. _A_ Which animal are you likely to find only in Australian chaparral?

13. _C_ Which condition does not contribute to fire in the chaparral?

14. _D_ Which animal is most important to cave ecosystems?

15. _C_ Which animals do not live in or visit caves?

16. _B_ Which sense is least useful inside a cave?

CHALLENGE QUESTIONS

Short answer:

17. List three ways that polar bears are designed to live in the tundra. **Layer of blubber, two coats of hair, webbed feet, white color, good swimmers, sharp claws, papillae on pads of feet.**

18. The largest hot desert in the world is the _**Sahara Desert**_.

19. Where is this desert located? **In northern Africa.**

20. How has this desert changed since the time of the Genesis Flood? **It used to be much wetter and supported animals such as elephants.**

21. List three major products that come from deserts. **Oil/petroleum, gold, diamonds, uranium, nickel, aluminum, sodium nitrate, copper, solar energy.**

22. What is the tallest mountain in the Himalayas? **Mt. Everest.**

23. Name three animals found only in the Himalayas. **Snow leopard, clouded leopard, Bengal tiger, red panda.**

24. List three possible fire cues for seed germination. **Heat, smoke, charred wood, oxidation, acids.**

25. What method do insect-eating bats use to find their food? **Echolocation.**

ANIMAL BEHAVIORS

LESSON 24

SEASONAL BEHAVIORS

IT HAPPENS EVERY YEAR

SUPPLY LIST

Research materials on monarch butterflies   Paper   Colored pencils

WHAT DID WE LEARN?

* What is hibernation? **A deep winter sleep in which the body's functions slow down greatly.**

* What is estivation? **A deep summer sleep similar to hibernation.**

* What is migration? **Moving from one location to another and then returning in order to survive the changing weather.**

* List three different kinds of animals that migrate. **Birds, whales, sea turtles, butterflies and other insects, caribou, salmon, etc.**

* What is the most likely trigger for seasonal behaviors? **The length of the day—changing number of hours of daylight.**

TAKING IT FURTHER

* How can animals know where they are supposed to go when they migrate if they have never been there before? **Some animals follow their parents, but many travel by instinct.**

* How do animals navigate while migrating? **Some use the stars, some follow scents, and others use landmarks.**

* Why might a group of animals move from one location to another, other than for their annual migration? **Changing climate conditions or natural disasters might make food scarce so animals will move to a new location. This is called immigration not migration because the animals do not usually return to the original location.**

* If you see a monarch butterfly in the fall and then see another one in the spring, how likely is it that you are seeing the same butterfly? **It depends where you live. If you live in Mexico, you might be seeing the butterfly when it arrives and when it leaves. But if you live in Canada, it is very unlikely that the same butterfly that flew south in the fall would ever live to make it back to the north.**

ECOSYSTEMS

LESSON 25 · ANIMAL DEFENSES

A MATTER OF PROTECTION

SUPPLY LIST

Card stock or tagboard   Drawing materials   Pictures of animals

WHAT DID WE LEARN?

- What are three main ways that animals try to defend themselves? **Flight, trickery, and fight.**

- List three ways that animals can trick their enemies into leaving them alone. **Intimidation, ink, inflating their bodies, camouflage, etc.**

- How do some eels protect themselves? **They can shock their predators with an electric pulse.**

TAKING IT FURTHER

- Why do you think animals prefer to run away or frighten off enemies rather than fight? **Fighting is more dangerous. Getting away or making the enemy leave is more likely to keep the animal alive.**

- Why do many animals prefer trickery to running away? **Trickery uses up less energy than running away.**

- How might a defense also serve as an attack method? **An animal may use its teeth or claws to protect itself from its enemies and then use the same teeth and claws to attack its own prey.**

LESSON 26 · ADAPTATION

FITTING IN

SUPPLY LIST

Copy of "How was I Designed?" worksheet

HOW WAS I DESIGNED? WORKSHEET

Organism	Design features
Jack rabbit	**Has large ears for greater heat dissipation in hot environments.**
Woodpecker	**Has toes going both directions to grasp tree; has shock absorbing skull for drilling; has sticky tongue for getting insects inside a tree.**
Orchid	**Has roots that can absorb water from the air so they can grow on the sides of trees where there is adequate sunlight.**
Honey bee	**Has pollen baskets to collect pollen when getting nectar from flowers.**
Cactus	**Has needles to prevent loss of water; have the ability to store large amounts of water.**
Brown Bat	**Uses echolocation for flying and for catching insects; designed to hang upside down for long periods of time.**
Oak tree	**Loses its leaves in the winter.**

Prairie grass	Has growing center near the ground so it can continue to grow even after being eaten over and over; goes dormant in winter.
Barn owl	Has great eyesight and hearing; has the ability to regurgitate indigestible materials.
Chameleon	Can change colors for camouflage and attracting mates.

WHAT DID WE LEARN?

- What is an adaptation? **A physical characteristic or behavior that allows an animal to surive in its environment.**

- Are all helpful characteristics a result of a change in the organism? **No, many characteristics were part of the original created organism.**

- What process causes different species to develop among the same kind of animal or plant? **The selection of adaptations through natural selection.**

TAKING IT FURTHER

- How does natural selection work? **A kind of animal or plant can produce offspring with many different characteristics. If a particular characteristic makes an animal better suited for its environment, it will be more likely to survive and reproduce. Those offspring are more likely to have the trait that was beneficial, so they will be better suited to the environment.**

- Does natural selection require millions of years to develop distinct populations? **No, all of the animals began reproducing after the original pairs left the Ark only a few thousand years ago, and have developed into the many species we see today. There have even been observed cases of speciation.**

- Does natural selection require genetic mutation? **No. The information for great variety was available in the original created kinds. That variety can be selected for without mutations, though mutations provide more variety for selection to act on.**

LESSON

27 BALANCE OF NATURE

KEEPING IT WORKING

SUPPLY LIST (OPTIONAL ACTIVITY)

Cooking pot   Grass   Distilled water   Jar   Microscope   Eyedropper
Microscope slides and cover slips   Copy of "Growing an Ecosystem" worksheet
pH testing paper

WHAT DID WE LEARN?

- What is meant by the balance of nature? **A state in which the producers and consumers are in equilibrium.**

- Name two ways that the balance of nature is maintained in an ecosystem. **Predator/prey feedback and territoriality are the main ways. Flocking also affects the balance.**

- What are two ways that an animal might stake out its territory? **Singing, demonstrations, and scent markings.**

- What happens if a male cannot find a territory to defend? **He does not mate and waits until a territory opens up.**

TAKING IT FURTHER

- What would be the likely effect on the ecosystem if a prairie dog colony was devastated by the plague? **Their primary predators, the black-footed ferrets, would begin to starve and would not reproduce as quickly, lowering their population as well.**

- What would happen if animals did not respect each others' territories? **Too many animals would breed in a given area and there would not be enough food for everyone and many would starve until balance was restored.**

- How does the oxygen cycle demonstrate the balance of nature? **The amount of oxygen and carbon dioxide produced and consumed by all the plants and animals in the world is about equal, showing balance.**

- Which methods of population control were created at the beginning and which have developed since the Fall? **Territoriality and flocking were likely created at the beginning; predator/prey feedback has developed since the Fall.**

QUIZ 5

ANIMAL BEHAVIORS

LESSONS 24–27

Mark each statement as either True or False.

1. _T_ Hibernation is a seasonal behavior for animals.
2. _F_ An animal's heartbeat is higher during hibernation.
3. _F_ Estivation occurs during the winter.
4. _T_ Butterflies often migrate hundreds of miles.
5. _T_ Migrating birds often fly in a V formation.
6. _F_ Trickery is most animals' first defense.
7. _F_ Most animals are defenseless against their enemies.
8. _T_ Camouflage is a good animal defense.
9. _T_ Prairie dogs can alert their colony to possible dangers.
10. _T_ Adaptation can be a physical characteristic or a behavior.
11. _F_ Natural selection does not really occur.
12. _T_ Animals can adapt because their DNA allows for great variety.
13. _F_ Man is needed to maintain a balance in most ecosystems.
14. _T_ When the predator population increases, the prey population decreases.
15. _T_ God designed territoriality as a way to control populations of animals.

Short answer:

16. Describe how territoriality helps control animal populations. **If a male cannot find an adequate open territory, he will not mate until one becomes available.**

17. Explain why bears do not truly hibernate. **Bears' metabolism does not significantly slow down, and a bear can be awakened during the winter so it is not truly hibernating.**

18. Describe one type of animal defense. **Flight, trickery, fighting, etc.**

19. Explain how adaptations are a result of creation and not evolution. **Adaptations are primarily a result of the variety put into DNA at creation, not because of evolutionary mutations accumulating to make new features.**

20. What is the most likely trigger for seasonal behaviors? **Change in the number of daylight hours.**

CHALLENGE QUESTIONS

Match the term with its definition.

21. **_B_** Plant defense against animals.

22. **_F_** Plant defense against weather.

23. **_I_** Species developing from common ancestor.

24. **_A_** Birds commonly used to support evolution.

25. **_C_** Ability of a species to survive better than others.

26. **_G_** Organisms with human-modified DNA.

27. **_H_** Chemicals used to kill unwanted animals.

28. **_E_** Chemical used to control malaria.

29. **_J_** Display done to attract a mate.

30. **_D_** Noise made by male elk to attract a mate.

UNIT 6
ECOLOGY & CONSERVATION

LESSON 28
MAN'S IMPACT ON THE ENVIRONMENT

WHERE DO WE FIT IN?

SUPPLY LIST

Copy of "How I Impact Nature" worksheet

WHAT DID WE LEARN?

- What are some ways that farmers impact ecosystems? **They clear the land, thus changing habitats; add chemicals to their crops killing insects and weeds; use water for irrigation.**

- What are some ways that farmers and ranchers have changed their practices to be more friendly to the environment? **Farming: contour farming, crop rotation, drip irrigation, wind breaks, GMOs, and organic farming; Ranching: introduce animals that compete with native animals for food, water, and space; sometimes kill predators.**

- What are some ways that industry impacts ecosystems? **Using land, adding pollutants to air and water, cutting down trees, using natural resources, etc.**

TAKING IT FURTHER

- What are some ways that people can minimize their impact on nature? **Recycle plastics, glass, and other items; reduce energy usage to reduce air pollution; grow plants without insecticides and herbicides.**

- How can hunting licenses positively affect man's impact on ecosystems? **Licenses limit the number of animals that can be hunted and limit the time of year that they can be hunted. This limits man's impact on the ecosystem. Also, when certain animal populations get too large, hunting can help to reduce them to sustainable sizes.**

LESSON 29
ENDANGERED SPECIES

ARE THEY DISAPPEARING?

SUPPLY LIST

Research materials on endangered species

WHAT DID WE LEARN?

- Name two possible natural causes of extinction of a species. **Climate change, disease, change in food supplies, etc.**

- Name three possible man-made causes of extinction of a species. **Habitat reduction, overhunting, pollution, harassment, etc.**

- Name three things people are doing to help endangered species. **Preserving or restoring habitat, reintroducing species, captive breeding, passing laws for protection, etc.**

TAKING IT FURTHER

- Why might people overhunt a particular animal? **To make money from the animals, to stop the animals from preying on livestock, to provide food for their families, etc.**

- Can people use the land without harming endangered species? **Since God said that man was to subdue and rule the earth, there is a way to be a good steward and still use the earth. It requires self-discipline which many people, companies, and/or nations lack.**

LESSON 30 POLLUTION

WHAT HAPPENED TO CLEAN AIR?

SUPPLY LIST

Rubber gloves   Newspaper   Bathroom scale   Copy of "Our Family's Trash" worksheet
One week of family trash

Supplies for Challenge: Clear plastic sheet protector   Sunscreen lotion   Newspaper
Modeling clay

WHAT DID WE LEARN?

- What is pollution? **The presence of any contaminant that harms the ecosystem.**

- What are some natural sources of pollution? **Sand storms, volcanoes, wildfires, oil seeps, etc.**

- What are some sources of man-made pollution? **Factories, automobiles, fireplaces, controlled burns, power plants, and trash.**

- What are three major areas of the environment that can become polluted? **Air, water, and land.**

TAKING IT FURTHER

- What are some ways that people can reduce water pollution? **Do not dump chemicals into the water, treat sewage, reduce the amounts of chemicals used in farming, remove oils from roads and parking lots so they are not washed away by rain.**

- What are some ways that people can reduce air pollution? **Use cleaner burning fuels, take chemicals out of the air before it is released from a factory, do not use dangerous chemicals, don't use your fireplace as much.**

- What are some ways that people can reduce land pollution? **Recycling, reducing the amount of wastes that are produced, reusing products.**

- Do you think that water, air and land is cleaner or dirtier today than it was 40 years ago? **In most parts of the world, the land, air, and water are significantly cleaner than they were 40 years ago.**

LESSON 31

ACID RAIN

DOES IT BURN?

SUPPLY LIST

2 identical houseplants 2 spray bottles Vinegar Water Copy of "Acid Rain" worksheet

WHAT DID WE LEARN?

- Why is rain naturally slightly acidic? **Water in the atmosphere combines with carbon dioxide to form carbonic acid.**
- What is acid rain? **Rain that has a level of acid higher than normal rain.**
- What are the main causes of acid rain? **Releasing of sulfur dioxide and nitrogen oxides from the burning of fossil fuels.**
- What is buffering capacity? **The ability of the soil to neutralize acid rain.**

TAKING IT FURTHER

- What are some ways to help reduce acid rain? **Reduce the sulfur dioxide and nitrogen oxides going into the air by using low sulfur coal, washing coal, scrubbing smoke, using less energy, and using alternative energy sources.**
- If the buffering capacity were the same, would you expect acid rain to be more of a problem or less of a problem in areas with high population densities? Why? **Where there are more people there is more need for energy, so more fossil fuels will be burned. Therefore, acid rain is more likely to be a problem in high-population areas.**

LESSON 32

GLOBAL WARMING

IS IT REALLY HEATING UP?

SUPPLY LIST

2 thermometers Glass jar with a lid Copy of "The Greenhouse Effect" worksheet
Supplies for Challenge: Poster board Drawing materials

WHAT DID WE LEARN?

- What is the greenhouse effect? **The atmosphere traps some of the sun's energy.**
- Why is the greenhouse effect important on earth? **It keeps the earth from being too cold.**
- What is global warming? **The increase of the average surface temperature of the earth.**
- What do many scientists claim are the two main causes of global warming? **Increased carbon dioxide due to the burning of fossil fuels and deforestation.**

Taking it further

- What are some ways that people might reduce the amount of carbon dioxide people are putting into the atmosphere? **Use less energy, change to alternative energy sources that do not use fossil fuels, and reduce deforestation.**

- Why is it inappropriate to panic about global warming? **First, we are all in God's hands and we must trust Him and not panic. Second, the data are not conclusive and the models are not reliable.**

LESSON 33

WHAT CAN YOU DO?

HOW CAN I HELP?

SUPPLY LIST

2 copies of "Three R's of Conservation" worksheet

WHAT DID WE LEARN?

- What are the three Rs of conservation? **Reduce, reuse, and recycle.**
- List two ways you plan to do each of these things. **Answers will vary.**

TAKING IT FURTHER

- Why is it important to be concerned about how humans impact the environment? **God has given people the job of caring for His creation and we need to take that job seriously.**

QUIZ 6

ECOLOGY & CONSERVATION

LESSONS 28–33

Identify each of the following as either natural (N), man-made (M), both (B), or unknown (U) in origin.

1. _N_ Cooler weather due to ash in the atmosphere from a volcanic eruption
2. _N_ Smoke in the air from a fire started by a lightning strike
3. _B_ Acid rain
4. _B_ Species extinction
5. _B_ Habitat reduction
6. _M_ Invasive species introduction
7. _M_ Captive breeding
8. _B_ Air pollution
9. _B_ Water pollution
10. _N_ Greenhouse effect

11. _U_ Global warming

12. _N_ Buffering capacity

13. _M_ Deforestation **(Accept B if natural disasters such as hurricanes are included.)**

14. _M_ Plastic recycling

15. _M_ Overhunting

Fill in the blank with the correct term.

16. The three Rs of conservation are **_reduce_**, **_reuse_**, and **_recycle_**.

17. Ranch animals must share **_land_**, **_food_**, and **_water_** with native animals.

18. Species that are no longer alive are said to be **_extinct_**.

19. The zebra mussel is considered an **_invasive_** species.

20. The most costly captive breeding program was to save the **_California condor_**.

21. Three main areas of pollution include **_air_**, **_water_**, and **_land_**.

22. **_Acid rain_** is caused by sulfur dioxide and nitrogen oxides in the air.

23. Materials that naturally decompose are said to be **_biodegradable_**.

24. An area's ability to neutralize acid rain is called its **_buffering capacity_**.

25. One thing I can do to help the environment is **_(accept reasonable answers)_**.

CHALLENGE QUESTIONS

Short answer:

26. Briefly describe a biblical view of ecology. **The earth belongs to God; man is His steward. We are to take care of and use the resources God has given us for our good and God's glory, without misusing them.**

27. List two government organizations that are committed to protecting the environment. **US Fish and Wildlife, EPA, US Park Service, United Nations FAO.**

28. Briefly explain how ozone depletion can occur. **CFCs rise in the atmosphere and UV radiation breaks off chlorine atoms which react with ozone to break it apart.**

29. List three alternative sources of energy which could replace fossil fuels. **Hydroelectric, solar, nuclear, wind, hydrogen cars, electric cars.**

30. Why are fossil fuels considered non-renewable resources? **Fossil fuels are not being made in any large quantities today.**

31. Explain two possible problems with plastic recycling. **People do not put forth efforts to recycle, some plastics are difficult to recycle, and it is more costly to recycle than to make new resin.**

32. Describe your plan for how you will be a good steward of God's environment. **Answers will vary.**

LESSON

34 REVIEWING ECOSYSTEMS: FINAL PROJECT

FINAL PROJECT SUPPLY LIST

Supplies will vary depending on project

FINAL EXAM

PROPERTIES OF ECOSYSTEMS

LESSONS 1–34

Match the term to its definition.

1. _C_ Flow of energy from one organism to another
2. _B_ Area of the earth containing life
3. _D_ Organisms which produce food
4. _E_ Non-living
5. _A_ The environment in which an organism lives
6. _G_ Ability of the soil to neutralize acid
7. _H_ Top layer of a forest
8. _I_ Living life primarily in trees
9. _F_ Grassland of Europe and Asia
10. _J_ Microscopic aquatic animals
11. _O_ Where fresh water flows into the ocean
12. _M_ Land along the banks of a river or stream
13. _N_ Coral reef formed around a sunken volcano
14. _L_ Deep sleep during the summer
15. _K_ Cavern in a mountain or underground
16. Draw a picture of a food chain with at least three links. **Answers will vary.**
17. Draw a picture of a food web with at least six different and interconnected organisms. **Answers will vary.**
18. Draw a picture of the water cycle. **See student manual, page 26.**
19. Put the organisms below in the ecosystem in which they are most likely to be found.

Tundra	Grassland	Rainforest	Ocean	Cave
Heather	**Sage**	**Lemon tree**	**Plankton**	**Millipede**
Ephemerals	**Grass**	**Pineapple**	**Algae**	**Bats**
Polar bear	**Zebra**	**Cocoa tree**	**Shark**	**Blind fish**
Caribou	**Gazelle**	**Monkey**	**Jellyfish**	
Ptarmigan	**Coyote**	**Tree frog**	**Octopus**	
	Bison	**Toucan**	**Crab**	
		Capybara		

20. List at least 3 characteristics of each of the following ecosystems.

Coral reef	Estuary	Deciduous forest	Desert	Mountain
Warm clear water **Near equator** **Great biodiversity** **Coral**	**Fresh and salt water meet** **Very productive** **Salt tolerant plants and animals**	**Deciduous trees** **30–60 in. rain/yr** **Cold winter** **Warm/wet summer**	**< 10 in. rain/yr** **Loses more moisture than gains** **Plant/animals conserve water** **Easily floods**	**Different ecosystems with altitude** **Has timberline and snow line** **Found everywhere in the world, even underwater**

Mark each statement as either True or False.

21. _T_ Many different animals exhibit seasonal behaviors.

22. _T_ Bears do not truly hibernate since they can wake up in the winter.

23. _F_ Monarch butterflies complete their migration in one generation.

24. _F_ Female birds are the ones that usually sing and defend their territory.

25. _T_ All animals were originally designed to eat plants.

26. _F_ Trickery is the first instinct most animals have for defending themselves.

27. _T_ Animals can use claws and teeth for defense.

28. _F_ Territoriality is the primary way that populations are controlled today.

29. _T_ Territoriality is the original way God designed population control.

30. _F_ Natural selection does not really occur.

31. _T_ Pollution can sometimes have natural causes.

32. _T_ Recycling is one way to help reduce man's impact on nature.

33. _F_ We should all panic about global warming.

34. _F_ Man is the only reason species become extinct.

35. _T_ People have made great progress in reducing acid rain.

CHALLENGE QUESTIONS

Fill in the blank with the correct term.

36. The maximum population an area can support is called its **_carrying capacity_**.

37. A **_ecotone_** is a transitional area between two ecosystems.

38. **_Pioneer_** plants are the first plants to move into an area after a natural disaster.

39. The final, stable ecosystem of a succession is called the **_climax_** ecosystem.

40. **_Mutualism_** is a relationship between two organisms in which both are benefited.

41. The land drained by a particular body of water is called a **_watershed_**.

42. **_Echolocation_** is the use of sound waves by bats to detect objects.

43. Behavior performed to attract a mate is called **_animal courtship_**.

44. **_Adaptive radiation_** refers to several species that develop from a common ancestor.

45. Ozone protects the earth from **_ultraviolet radiation_** or **solar radiation_**.

46. **_CFCs/chlorofluorocarbons_** are the molecules that are believed to cause ozone destruction.

47. Plastics are made from molecules called **_polymers_**.

48. Resources that cannot be replaced are **_non-renewable resources_**.

Short answer:

49. Draw a population pyramid for an aquatic ecosystem. **See student manual, page 21.**

50. Describe a possible succession for an area of pine forest after a forest fire. **Small flowering plants will grow first, followed by grass and small shrubs; eventually larger shrubs will crowd out the smaller plants; finally trees will crowd out most of the grass and smaller shrubs.**

51. Draw a cross section of a tree trunk. Label all parts. **See student manual, page 41.**

52. List at least three commercial products from the desert. **Oil/petroleum, gold, diamonds, uranium, nickel, aluminum, sodium nitrate, copper, solar energy.**

53. Explain how some plants can germinate only when there is a fire. **Some seeds require heat, smoke, or charring before they will germinate so a fire is necessary for germination.**

54. Describe one animal courtship ritual you found interesting. **Answers will vary.**

LESSON 35

CONCLUSION

APPRECIATING OUR ORDERLY WORLD

SUPPLY LIST

Bible   Writing materials

ECOSYSTEMS

APPENDICES

APPENDICES

RESOURCE GUIDE

Many of the following titles are available from Answers in Genesis (www.AnswersBookstore.com).

PROPERTIES OF ATOMS & MOLECULES

Suggested Books

Structure of Matter by Mark Galan in the *Understanding Science and Nature* series from Time-Life Books—Lots of real-life applications of chemistry

Inventions and Inventors series from Grolier Educational—Many interesting articles

Molecules by Janice VanCleave—Fun activities

Chemistry for Every Kid by Janice VanCleave—More fun activities

Science Lab in a Supermarket by Bob Friedhoffer—Fun kitchen chemistry

Science and the Bible by Donald B. DeYoung—Great biblical applications of scientific ideas

200 Gooey, Slippery, Slimy, Weird & Fun Experiments by Janice VanCleave—More fun activities

Suggested Videos

Newton's Workshop by Moody Institute—Excellent Christian science series; several titles to choose from

Chemicals to Living Cell: Fantasy or Science (DVD) by Dr. Jonathan Sarfati—The laws of real chemistry show why "goo-to-you" evolution is impossible

Field Trip Ideas

- Visit the Creation Museum in Petersburg, Kentucky
- Visit a greenhouse or hydroponics operation to see the use of chemicals with plants
- Tour a battery store to learn about different types of batteries
- Visit a film processing plant to learn about chemicals in film processing or photo printing
- Visit a pharmacy
- Tour an injection molding plant to learn more about plastics
- Visit a farm to learn about the use of chemicals in farming

PROPERTIES OF MATTER

Suggested Books

Structure of Matter by Mark Galan in the *Understanding Science and Nature* series from Time-Life Books—Lots of real-life applications of Chemistry

Inventions and Inventors series from Grolier Educational—Many interesting articles

Soda Pop by Arlene Erlbach—Fun look inside a soda pop factory

Molecules by Janice VanCleave—Lots of fun activities

Chemistry for Every Kid by Janice VanCleave—More fun activities

Science Lab in a Supermarket by Bob Friedhoffer—Fun kitchen chemistry

Science and the Bible, Volumes 1–3 by Donald B. DeYoung—Many experiments with great biblical applications of scientific ideas

Exploring the World of Chemistry by John Hudson Tiner—An exciting and intriguing tour of chemistry with facts and stories about the discoveries and discoverers

Suggested Videos

Newton's Workshop by Moody Institute—Excellent Christian science series; several titles to choose from

Chemicals to Living Cell: Fantasy or Science (DVD) by Dr. Jonathan Sarfati—The laws of real chemistry show why "goo-to-you" evolution is impossible

Field Trip Ideas

- Visit the Creation Museum in Petersburg, Kentucky
- Visit a bakery
- Visit a soft drink manufacturer
- Visit a dairy farm to see where milk comes from
- Visit a dairy bottling plant to see what happens to the milk after the farm
- Visit a freshwater treatment plant
- Visit a wastewater treatment plant

PROPERTIES OF ECOSYSTEMS

Suggested Books

Kingfisher Illustrated Animal Encyclopedia—Information on over 1000 animals

Marvels of Creation series by Buddy and Kay Davis—Creationist view of various animals

North American Wildlife from Reader's Digest—Our favorite field guide

Zoo Guide, Aquarium Guide, Museum Guide by Answers in Genesis—A must-have for trips to evolutionary locations, each guide provides creation perspectives to read at each exhibit

Suggested Videos/CDs

Lyrical Life Science—Old folk tunes with new words to help teach vocabulary

Backyard Bird Song CD—Teaches how to identify birds by their songs

Explore the Wildlife Kingdom Series—Fun nature videos; six differend DVDs to choose from

Incredible Creatures that Defy Evolution Vol. 1–3—Examines design features of many different animals

Newton's Workshop: Pollution Solution—Live action DVD with fun stories for all ages

Field Trip Ideas

- Visit the Creation Museum in Petersburg, Kentucky
- Visit as many different ecosystems as you can
- Zoo
- Aquarium
- Natural history museum
- Hydroelectric plant
- Power plant
- Solar energy or wind energy plant
- National park

CREATION SCIENCE RESOURCES

Exploring the World Around You by Gary Parker—More detailed look at different aspects of ecology

Answers Book for Kids Four volumes by Ken Ham with Cindy Malott—Answers children's frequently asked questions

Creation: Facts of Life by Gary Parker—Good explanation of the evidence for creation

The Young Earth by John D. Morris PhD—Evidence for a young earth

The New Answers Book 1 & 2 by Ken Ham and others—Answers frequently asked questions

Zoo Guide and *Aquarium Guide* by Answers in Genesis—A biblical look at animals, including extinction, defense/attack structures, biomes, and stewardship

MASTER SUPPLY LIST

The following table lists all the supplies used for *God's Design for Chemistry & Ecology* activities. You will need to look up the individual lessons in the student book to obtain the specific details for the individual activities (such as quantity, color, etc.). The letter *c* denotes that the lesson number refers to the challenge activity. Common supplies such as colored pencils, construction paper, markers, scissors, tape, etc., are not listed.

Supplies needed (see lessons for details)	Atoms/Molecules	Matter	Ecosystems
3-ring binder			2
Alka-Seltzer	17c, 20c		
Alum (in spice section)		28	
Ammonia (clear)	23, 23c		
Antacid tablets or liquid	23, 24		
Bag (produce)			19
Baking soda	1, 12c, 17, 23	6c, 10, 17, 20, 22c, 24c, 25, 29, 34	
Balloon (helium-filled, optional)		9c	
Balloons (latex)	30, 33	2, 6c, 15, 35	
Banana	26c		
Battery (6-volt)		17	
Battery (9-volt)	12c		
Bean seeds		18c	
Bible	35		
Block (wooden)		12	
Borax	31c, 32c		
Bottle (plastic ½-gallon or 1-liter)		15c, 20	
Box (small)		3, 7	18 , 23
Bread	28	30, 33c	
Cabbage (red/purple)	21		
Cake mix		23c	
Candle	9, 10, 17	20, 35	
Charcoal briquettes		28	
Cinnamon		25	
Club soda		25	
Coffee filter		19	
Copper sulfate (available at swimming pool supply store)	32c		
Corn syrup		25	
Cornstarch	31c	34	
Cotton balls		28	18, 21

Supplies needed (see lessons for details)	Atoms/Molecules	Matter	Ecosystems
Cups (clear)	17c	3, 9, 22, 22c, 24, 26c, 28	15, 16
Cups (foam)	20c		
Cups (paper)	12c	5, 6	
Diaper (disposable)	34		
Dish soap	10c, 23, 34	13, 15c, 24c	
Dividers (folder)			2
Dry ice	10		
Earthworms			2
Eggs	7, 20	23, 23c, 27	
Epsom salt	15, 32c		
Eraser		8c	
Eyedropper	34		15, 27
Field guide to flowering plants			8
Flashlight with battery	6		
Flour		30, 33	
Food coloring	34	25	12, 15
Funnel		19	
Garlic powder	28		
Gelatin	25c		
Geode (optional)	15		
Ginger ale	28		
Glitter	32		
Gloves (leather and cotton)	10		18
Gloves (rubber)			30
Goggles		28	14
Golf ball		8	
Grass and other plants	27		6, 8, 8c, 21, 23, 27, 31
Hammer		28	14
Hand lotion		13	
Hand mirror		11	
Hole punch		5	
Honey		12, 13	
Hydrogen peroxide	19		
Ice			18
Ice tray		11	
Iodine		30, 34	
Jar (with lid)	17, 20, 22c, 29	11c, 17, 20, 21	2, 6, 27, 32
Jigsaw puzzle		16	

Supplies needed (see lessons for details)	Atoms/Molecules	Matter	Ecosystems
Leaves			20, 21
Lemon juice	19, 22, 24	10, 23, 25, 32	
Life Savers candies (roll)		22, 31c	
Magnifying glass			1, 5, 14
Marbles	25c	8c, 9c	
Margarine	8, 28	1, 33	
Marshmallows (mini, colored)	11, 12, 13		
Matches	9, 10, 17		
Mentos candies	1c		
Meter stick/metric ruler		1, 3, 4, 5, 7	1, 8
Microscope and slides (optional)		3c	27
Milk (not skim)	22, 34	21c, 26, 31, 33	
Milk jug (1-gallon)		15	
Modeling clay	15c, 17	9, 9c	13, 30c
Molasses		2	
Mustard (dry)		23	
Newspaper			8, 21, 30, 30c
Oats			2
Oil (olive)	12c		
Oil (spray)		33	
Oil (vegetable)	8	9,13, 23, 24c, 30, 34	
Orange juice		19, 25	
Page protectors/sheet protectors			8, 30c
Paint			21
Paper bag (brown)		30	
Paper clips	22c	4, 5, 8	
Paper towels	34		
Paprika		23	
Peanut butter	8	30	
Pennies	22c	5, 8	
Perfume		14c	
pH testing paper (optional)			27
Photos of animals			18, 25
Pineapple juice (fresh, not frozen)	25c		
Pinecones	32c		
Ping-pong ball		8	
Plant food	27		
Plaster of Paris	15c		
Plastic bottles (empty 2-liter)		2, 6c, 18c, 28	
Plastic zipper bags	26c, 34	22, 26, 28, 33c	14, 20

Supplies needed (see lessons for details)	Atoms/Molecules	Matter	Ecosystems
Plate (ceramic)	9		
Polymer clay (Femo, Sculpey, etc.)	16		
Popcorn		9	
Potassium salt (in spice section)	32c	22c, 24c	
Potato	19		
Potato or tortilla chips		30	
Pots and pans			12, 27
Potting soil		18c	6
Powdered sugar		34	
Pudding mix (instant)		31	
Rocks		12, 28	14
Rolling pin		22	
Rubber band	30	5	
Rubbing alcohol	29	9, 34	
Safety goggles			14
Salt	12c, 15, 22c, 24, 32c	10, 22c, 23, 24c, 26, 26c, 27, 33	15, 16
Sand		28	2, 14
Scale (bathroom)			30
Scale (gram)		6c	
Seashells			14
Silver object (tarnished)	14		
Silver polish/tarnish remover	14		
Soft drink (canned, diet & regular)		24, 25c	
Soft drink (lemon lime)	22		
Soft drink (diet 2-liter bottle)	1c		
Soil		28	2, 6
Spices (ginger root, mint leaves, cinnamon sticks, allsp ice, cloves, peppermint oil, almond extract, etc.)	29, 29c	25	
Spoon (metal)		1, 8c, 12	
Spoon (wooden)		1	
Spray bottles			31
Starch (liquid)	34		
Steel wool without soap	10c, 20		
Stopwatch	17c, 20c	1, 3, 26c	
Straw	33	27	
String	33	5, 18c	1
Sugar	12c	2, 21, 22c, 24c, 25, 26, 33	
Sugar cubes		6	

Supplies needed (see lessons for details)	Atoms/Molecules	Matter	Ecosystems
Sunscreen lotion			30c
Swabs	24		
Tagboard/card stock/poster board			7c, 8, 20c, 25, 32c
Tape (electrical or duct)	6, 33		
Tape (masking)		2, 3, 5	
Tape measure (cloth)		2, 15c	
Telescope (optional)		3c	
Tennis ball		3, 7c, 14	
Test tubes	10c		
Thermometer	20	2, 3, 26c	16, 32
Tissue paper or quilt batting			18
Toothpaste (with fluoride)	7, 23		
Toothpicks	1c, 11, 12, 13		
Vanilla extract		21, 25, 26	
Vinegar	1, 7, 17, 20, 22, 23c, 25c	6c, 20, 21c,23, 34	31
Water (distilled)	12c, 23c		27
Whipped cream (spray can)		21	
Whipping cream (liquid)		21	
Wire (copper)	6, 12c	17	
World atlas			1c, 7, 17
Yeast	26c	2, 33	

WORKS CITED

PROPERTIES OF ATOMS & MOLECULES

"Alexander Fleming." http://www.pbs.org/wgbh/aso/databank/entries/bmflem.html.

Biddle, Verne. *Chemistry Precision and Design*. Pensacola: A Beka Book Ministry, 1986.

"Bioceramics." http://www.azom.com/details.asp?ArticleID=1743.

Brice, Raphaelle. *From Oil to Plastic*. New York: Young Discovery Library, 1985.

"Buckyballs." http://scifun.chem.wisc.edu/chemweek/buckball/buckball.html.

"Charles Goodyear and the Strange Story of Rubber." *Reader's Digest*. Pleasantville, N.Y.: January 1958.

"Charles Martin Hall." http://www.geocities.com/bio-electrochemistry/hall.htm.

"Charles Martin Hall and the Electrolytic Process for Refining Aluminum." http://www.oberlin.edu/chem/history/cmharticle.html.

"Charles Martin Hall. "http://www.corrosion-doctors.org/Biographies/HallBio.htm.

"Chemotherapy, What it is, How it Helps." http://www.cancer.org/docroot/ETO/content/ETO_1_2X_Chemotherapy_What_It_Is_How_It_Helps.asp.

Chisholm, Jane, and Mary Johnson. *Introduction to Chemistry*. London: Usborne Publishing, 1983.

Cobb, Vicki. *Chemically Active Experiments You Can Do at Home*. New York: J.B. Lippincott, 1985.

Cooper, Christopher. *Matter*. New York: Dorling Kindersley, 1992.

"Development of the Periodic Table." http://mooni.fccj.org/~ethall/period/period.htm.

"Diapers, the Inside Story." http://portal.acs.org/portal/fileFetch/C/CSTA_014946/pdf/CSTA_014946.pdf.

Dineen, Jacqueline. *Plastics*. Hillside: Enslow Publishers Inc., 1988.

Dunsheath, Percy. *Giants of Electricity*. New York: Thomas Y. Crowell Co., 1967.

"Enzyme Chemistry." http://www.math.unl.edu/%7Ejump/Center1/Labs/EnzymeChemistry.pdf?id=11897.

"Farming , Food and Biotechnology." *Inventions and Inventors*. 2000.

Galan, Mark. *Structure of Matter - Understanding Science and Nature*. Alexandria: Time-Life Books, 1992.

Helmenstine, Anne Marie, Ph.D. "Chemistry." http://chemistry.about.com.

"Historical Development of the Periodic Table." http://members.tripod.com/~EppE/historyp.htm.

"How and Why Science in the Water." *World Book*. 1998.

"How Does a Halogen Light Bulb Work?" http://home.howstuffworks.com/question151.htm.

Hughey, Pat. *Scavengers and Decomposers: The Cleanup Crew*. New York: Atheneum, 1984.

Jenkins, John E., and George Mulfinger, Jr. *Basic Science for Christian Schools*. Greenville: Bob Jones University Press, 1983.

Julicher, Kathleen. *Experiences in Chemistry*. Baytown: Castle Heights Press, 1997.

Kuklin, Susan. *Fireworks: the Science, the Art, and the Magic*. New York: Hyperion Books for Children, 1996.

"Medicine and Health." *Inventions and Inventors*. 2000.

Morris, John D., Ph.D. *The Young Earth*. Green Forest: Master Books, 1998.

Newmark, Ann. *Chemistry*. New York: Dorling Kindersley, 1993.

Parker, Gary. *Creation Facts of Life*. Colorado Springs: Master Books, 1994.

Parker, Steve. *Look at Your Body - Digestion*. Brookfield: Copper Beech books, 1996.

"Penny For Your Thoughts." http://www.tryscience.org/experiments/experiments_pennythoughts_athome.html.

Pinkerton, J.C. "Alexander Fleming and the Discovery of Penicillin." http://nh.essortment.com/alexander-flemin_rmkm.htm.

"Polymers: They're Everywhere." http://www.nationalgeographic.com/resources/ngo/education/plastics/nature.html.

Richards, Jon. *Chemicals and Reactions*. Brookfield: Copper Beech books, 2000.

Saari, Peggy and Stephen Allison, Eds. *Scientists: The Lives and Works of 150 Scientists*. U.X.L An Imprint of Gale, 1996.

"Silly Putty." http://www.chem.umn.edu/outreach/Sillyputty.html.

Solids, Liquids, and Gases. Ontario Science Center. Toronto: Kids Can Press, 1998.

Steele, DeWitt. *Observing God's World*. Pensacola: A Beka Books Publishers, 1978.

Student Activities in Basic Science for Christian Schools. Greenville: Bob Jones University Press, 1994.

Thomas, Peggy. *Medicines from Nature.* New York: Twenty-First Century Books, 1997.

VanCleave, Janice. *Chemistry for Every Kid.* New York: John Wiley and Sons, Inc., 1989.

VanCleave, Janice. *Molecules.* New York: John Wiley and Sons, Inc., 1993.

"Vulcanized Rubber." http://inventors.about.com/library/inventors/blrubber.htm.

"WebElements Periodic Table of the Elements." http://www.webelements.com/index.html.

Wile, Jay. *Exploring Creation with Chemistry.* Anderson: Apologia Educational Ministries, 2003.

PROPERTIES OF MATTER

Ardley, Meil. *Making Metric Measurements.* New York: Franklin Watts, 1983.

Better Homes and Gardens New Cook Book. Des Moines: Merideth Corporation, 1981.

"BHA and BHT." http://chemistry.about.com/library/weekly/aa082101a.htm.

Biddle, Verne. *Chemistry Precision and Design.* Pensacola: A Beka Book Ministry, 1986.

Brice, Raphaelle. *From Oil to Plastic.* New York: Young Discovery Library, 1985.

Busenberg, Bonnie. *Vanilla, Chocolate, and Strawberry, The Story of Your Favorite Flavors.* Minneapolis: Lerner Publications Co., 1994.

"The Chemistry of Cakes." http://www.margarine.org.uk/pg_app2.htm.

Chisholm, Jane, and Mary Johnson. *Introduction to Chemistry.* London: Usborne Publishing, 1983.

Cobb, Vicki. *Chemically Active Experiments You Can Do at Home.* New York: J.B. Lippincott, 1985.

Cooper, Christopher. *Matter.* New York: Dorling Kindersley, 1992.

"Desalination of Water." *Columbia Encyclopedia.* 2000.

DeYoung, Donald B. *Science and the Bible.* Grand Rapids: Baker Books, 1994.

Dineen, Jacqueline. *Plastics.* Hillside: Enslow Publishers Inc., 1988.

Dunsheath, Percy. *Giants of Electricity.* New York: Thomas Y. Crowell Co., 1967.

"Energy Value of Food." http://www.cristina.prof.ufsc.br/digestorio/mcardle_energy_value_food_ch4_connection.pdf.

Erlbach, Arlene. *Soda Pop.* Minneapolis: Lerner Publications Co., 1994.

"Farming, Food and Biotechnology." *Inventions and Inventors.* 2000.

"Fleischmann's Yeast: Best-Ever Breads." Birmingham: Time Inc. Ventures Custom Publishing, 1993.

"The Flour Page." http://www.cookeryonline.com/Bread/flour.html.

Friedhoffer, Bob. *Science Lab in a Supermarket.* New York: Franklin Watts, 1998.

Galan, Mark. *Structure of Matter: Understanding Science and Nature.* Alexandria: Time-Life Books, 1992.

Groleau, Rick. "Buoyancy Brainteasers." http://www.pbs.org/wgbh/nova/lasalle/buoyancy.html.

"History." http://www.breadinfo.com/history.shtml.

"How and Why: Science in the Water." *World Book.* 1998.

"How Does a Water Softener Work?" http://home.howstuffworks.com/question99.htm.

"How Sweet It Is!" http://portal.acs.org/portal/fileFetch/C/CSTA_015104/pdf/CSTA_015104.pdf.

Hughey, Pat. *Scavengers and Decomposers: The Cleanup Crew.* New York: Atheneum, 1984.

Jenkins, John E., and George Mulfinger, Jr. *Basic Science for Christian Schools.* Greenville: Bob Jones University Press, 1983.

Julicher, Kathleen. *Experiences in Chemistry.* Baytown: Castle Heights Press, 1997.

Kuklin, Susan. *Fireworks: the Science, the Art, and the Magic.* New York: Hyperion Books for Children, 1996.

Mebane, Robert C., and Thomas R. Rybolt. *Air and Other Gases.* New York: Twenty-first Century Books, 1995.

"Medicine and Health." *Inventions and Inventors.* 2000.

Morris, John D., Ph.D. *The Young Earth.* Colorado Springs: Master Books, 1992.

Newmark, Ann. *Chemistry.* New York: Dorling Kindersley, 1993.

Nottridge, Rhoda. *Additives.* Minneapolis: Carolrhoda Books Inc., 1993.

Parker, Gary. *Creation: Facts of Life.* Colorado Springs: Master Books, 1994.

Parker, Steve. *Look at Your Body—Digestion.* Brookfield: Copper Beech books, 1996.

"Recipes Around the World." http://www.ivu.org/recipes.

Richards, Jon. *Chemicals and Reactions.* Brookfield: Copper Beech books, 2000.

Saari, Peggy and Stephen Allison, Eds. *Scientists: The Lives and Works of 150 Scientists*. U.X.L An Imprint of Gale, 1996.

Solids, Liquids, and Gases. Ontario Science Center. Toronto: Kids Can Press, 1998.

Stancel, Colette, and Keith Graham. *Biology God's Living Creation Field and Laboratory Manual*. Pensacola: A Beka Books, 1998.

Steele, DeWitt. *Observing God's World*. Pensacola: A Beka Books Publishers, 1978.

Student Activities in Basic Science for Christian Schools. Greenville: Bob Jones University Press, 1994.

Thomas, Peggy. *Medicines from Nature*. New York: Twenty-First Century Books, 1997.

VanCleave, Janice. *Chemistry for Every Kid*. New York: John Wiley and Sons, Inc., 1989.

VanCleave, Janice. *Molecules*. New York: John Wiley and Sons, Inc., 1993.

Walpole, Brenda. *Water*. Ada, OK: Garrett Educational Corp., 1990.

"William Prout." *Classic Encyclopedia*. http://www.1911encyclopedia.org/William_Prout.

Ziegler, Sandra. *A Visit to the Bakery*. Chicago: Children's Press, 1987.

PROPERTIES OF ECOSYSTEMS

"A Walk in the Forest." http://nationalzoo.si.edu/Education/ConservationCentral/walk/default.cfm.

"About the Dolphins." http://www.virtualexplorers.org/ARD/Dolphin/bkgd.htm.

"Alexander von Humboldt." http://geography.about.com/od/historyofgeography/a/vonhumboldt.htm.

"Alexander von Humboldt." http://www.humboldt.edu/~german/Alex.

"Alexander von Humboldt." http://www.phfawcettsweb.org/von.htm.

"Amazon River Animals." http://www.destination360.com/south-america/brazil/amazon-animals.php.

"Amazon." *Microsoft® Encarta® Online Encyclopedia*. http://encarta.msn.com/encyclopedia_761571466/Amazon_(river).html.

"Anaconda." *Microsoft® Encarta® Online Encyclopedia*. http://encarta.msn.com/encyclopedia_761553417/Anaconda_(snake).html.

"Animal Courtship Quiz." http://reference.aol.com/planet-earth/discovery/animal-courtship.

"Balance of Nature—Food Chains 101." http://www.hawkquest.org/TA/XL/Foodchain.pdf.

"Beach Exploratio." http://www.wetlandsinstitute.org/education/teacher/Beach_Exploration.pdf.

"Climate Change." http://www.epa.gov/climatechange/basicinfo.html.

"Coastal Ecosystems." http://www.soest.hawaii.edu/SEA-GRANT/bmpm/coastal_ecosystems.html.

"Coral Reef Bleaching." http://www.marinebiology.org/coralbleaching.htm.

"Ecohysteria." http://www.apologiaonline.com/conf/ecohyst.pdf.

"Epiphytes." http://rainforests.mongabay.com/0405.htm.

"Facts About Endangered Species." http://www.endangeredspecie.com/Interesting_Facts.htm.

"Food Chains and Pyramids." http://www.mostateparks.com/onondaga/foodchain.htm.

Great Lakes Basin Ecosystem Team, US Fish and Wildlife Service. http://www.fws.gov/midwest/greatlakes.

"Great Lakes Fact Sheet." http://www.epa.gov/glnpo/factsheet.html.

"How Great is the Amazon River?" http://www.extreme-science.com/AmazonRiver.htm.

"'Instant' Evolution Seen in Darwin's Finches, Study Says." http://news.nationalgeographic.com/news/2006/07/060714-evolution.html.

"Is Bleaching Coral's Way of Making the Best of a Bad Situation?" http://news.nationalgeographic.com/news/2001/07/0725_coralbleaching.html.

"Life in the Arctic Tundra." http://teacher.scholastic.com/products/instructor/Jan04_tundra.htm.

"Movie Review: Arctic Tale—Exaggerating the Effects of Global Warming." http://www.answersingenesis.org/articles/aid/v2/n1/arctic-tale.

"Ocean Science Activities." http://www.angelfire.com/la/kinderthemes/oscience.html.

Parker, Gary. *Exploring the World Around You*. Green Forest: Master Books, 2003.

"Peary, Robert E." http://www.pabook.libraries.psu.edu/palitmap/bios/Peary__Robert_Edwin.html.

"Recycling Plastics." http://www.eia.doe.gov/kids/energyfacts/saving/recycling/solidwaste/plastics.html.

"River Systems of the World." http://www.rev.net/~aloe/river.

"River." *Microsoft® Encarta® Online Encyclopedia*. http://encarta.msn.com/encyclopedia_761569915/river.html.

"Robert Peary." http://www.u-s-history.com/pages/h3896.html.

"The Emergence of Modern America." http://www.archives.gov/exhibits/american_originals/modern.html.

"The Estuary Ecosystem." http://www.teara.govt.nz/Earth-SeaAndSky/MarineEnvironments/Estuaries/2/en.

"The Great River Amazon." http://hubpages.com/hub/THE-GREAT-RIVER-AMAZON.

"The Living Forest." http://www.arborday.org/trees/ringsLivingForest.cfm.

"The Tundra Biome." http://www.ucmp.berkeley.edu/exhibits/biomes/tundra.php.

"Theodore Roosevelt." http://edhelper.com/Biography-ReadingComprehension_23_1.html.

"Theodore Roosevelt." http://www.desertusa.com/mag98/july/papr/du_troosev.html.

"Theodore Roosevelt." http://www.spiritus-temporis.com/theodore-roosevelt/presidency.html.

"Theodore Roosevelt." http://www.whitehouse.gov/history/presidents/tr26.html.

VanCleave, Janice. *Ecology for Every Kid*. New York: John Wiley & Sons, 1996.

Wilkes, Angela. *Usborne Book of Wild Places*. London: Usborne Publishing, 1990.